LOVE IS MY VOCATION

"He led her about and taught her, and he kept her as the apple of his eye. As an eagle he has spread his wings and hath taken her on his shoulder. The Lord alone was her leader."

DEUT. XXXII. 10-12

An Imaginative Story of
St. Thérèse of Lisieux

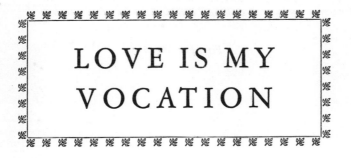

LOVE IS MY VOCATION

Tom Clarkson

FARRAR, STRAUS AND YOUNG

NEW YORK, NEW YORK

Acknowledgments

My thanks are due to:

The nuns of the Lisieux Carmel (especially the "unknown" with whom I was granted an interview) for their encouragement and prayers.

Mother St. Michael of the Blessed Trinity, Prioress of the Berkhamsted Carmel, and Sister Teresa of the Child Jesus, Sub-Prioress of the Chichester Carmel, for information about the Carmelite Order.

Messrs. Sheed and Ward, London, for permission to quote from Mr. F. J. Sheed's translation of *The Collected Letters of St. Thérèse.*

The Very Reverend Canon T. N. Taylor for permission to quote from his translation of St. Thérèse's autobiography.

Monsignor Vernon Johnson for useful introductions.

The Reverend Doctor Gordon Albion for further information.

Mlle. Andrée Renault for using her influence on my behalf.

Mr. Denys Blakelock for the loan of a precious relic of St. Thérèse.

Miss Eleanor Farjeon for helping with the revision of the manuscript.

I must also acknowledge my indebtedness to Father Henri Petitot's book, *St. Thérèse of Lisieux,* and to Father S.-J. Piat's book, *The Story of a Family.*

T. C.

Contents

PART THREE

The Gates of Heaven

PART ONE

The Secret Garden

❦

CHAPTER ONE

Entrance on a Snow-cloud

I

THE GLITTERING PROCESSION of the Second Empire, led by
its exotic Emperor and Empress, with their retinue like a court
of gilded flowers, nodding their silly perfumed heads in time
to some wild and irresponsible air of Offenbach, is passing
out of sight under the romantic trees of the *Bois,* the dreamy
lace-like trees of a *fête champêtre* which have suddenly turned
into cannon.

A dramatic boom, and a curtain of acrid smoke falls across
the tail of the pageant, blotting it out for ever.

When it rises the Third Republic has come into power.

The long straight boulevards of Baron Haussman are occu-
pied by a seeming democratic earnestness, which is probably no
less vicious, no less cruel, than the decadence that went before
it.

A so to speak new persecution is in vogue. Schools are forbidden to give religious instruction. Those convenient scape-
goats the Jesuits have been driven into the wilderness once
more. The capital, recovering from a diet of dogs and rats, is
seeking about for the means to repair her complexion. Soon the
old swings and roundabouts of the world will be rising and
falling and turning again. . . .

But we are travelling in another direction. We are going
down into the provinces, into lower Normandy, to the small
lace-making town of Alençon, where life has to be got on with
in spite of governments.

The flat monotonous landscape, woven with a pattern of
little orchards, farm-dwellings, and large puggish cows, un-

winds as from a bobbin. It was probably much the same then as it is now, although Alençon did not escape the universal bombardment. Today there are certain structural alterations, three cinemas, the ogre château turned into a prison, but the same atmosphere of conventional bourgeois respectability remains.

You could not call it exactly charming, it is too uncompromising for that, but it has a quality. The light is clear. The tall stone houses are clean. The women still kneel at the river to pound their laundry, and the men still patiently fish from the little bridge. The designs for the lace have become rather starker, more contemporary, but the intricate workmanship, as of civilized spiders, remains.

2

But it is January, the year 1873. . . .

Snow is falling. When we look up it is like whirling grey feathers, but to the woman lying in the four-poster, in the minute house in the Rue St. Blaise, the lamp already lit because it has grown dark so early, it is thick banks of twilight-blue piling up on the roofs opposite, white slanting drifts against her window-panes.

Zélie Martin is forty-two. She is still handsome, lying back in the deep coarse linen pillows, although the firm oval of her face, sided by its smooth black wings of hair—if there are any white ones they are unnoticeable—has become tautened and bloomless. She is feeding a cancer. . . . But it is not this illness which has brought her to bed today . . . not yet.

Marie is downstairs in the parlor with her three sisters. She is thirteen, Pauline is eleven. They are on holiday from the convent boarding-school at Le Mans. Léonie is ten, Céline is four. These are the surviving offspring of a family of eight, and there will be one more.

All these girls are destined to become nuns, but at present they are merely children at home in the late afternoon of winter.

We are to imagine a typical interior of the period, not quite so cluttered and draped as most perhaps, because this is Normandy, and the Martins are somewhat austere.

There is a round claw-footed table in the centre with small straight-backed chairs, two rather stiff wooden armchairs, a square oak dresser or sideboard, its lower doors heavily carved with a design of birds in foliage. They are pheasants perhaps, because the Normans are fond of drawing hunting motifs. There is a bobble-fringed mantel-board with a marble clock in the middle, flanked by two painted glass lamps. The wallpaper is dark red damask, and the hangings of bottle-green brocade. The pictures could be reproductions of religious subjects, historical engravings, a portrait or two of Louis Martin's military ancestors. No samplers. Little fingers in this part of the world are more seriously employed, although, at this moment, Pauline, who possesses an artistic talent, is painting a flower-piece, from memory, carefully drawn and tinted poppies and cornflowers bound with stalks of wheat.

But this also is to serve a useful purpose. There is a space for lettering, already faintly pencilled. It is to be a text.

She works intently, her thick dark hair fallen forward in a way Madame Martin would not approve of, so that we only glimpse her face when she raises it to dip the pointed brush in the jar of water. She has the straight brows and small piquant nose common to the rest of them, but she looks more practical then artistic, is probably one of those plain creative creatures who search elsewhere for a beauty they do not possess in themselves. She has a talent, but it is no more than that.

Indeed, every tendency in this family is subservient to one thing.

Marie is stitching a tiny bonnet, no bigger than a *demi-tasse*. It is sparkling white and crimped, as the snow will be in the morning on the window-ledges, trodden by the forks of birds.

She does not know she is taking part in the creation of a relic . . . all that is to come later.

She too is dark, with thick furry brows, a heavy oval face, and a sensitive generous mouth, possesses a maternal air, which is going to be needed. . . .

Léonie, against the window, doing nothing, peering round the blind, and kicking a pedestal with one button-booted foot, the only disturbance in the room, for the breathing of the small fire—it is surely a little too small for the time of year?—and the busy ticking of the clock are no more than threads in the texture of the atmosphere—Léonie is curiously apart. Her coloring is lighter, but it is not that. The other girls have open expressions, Léonie's is shut, turned in on herself. Her lips are thinner, wry-looking, and her brow contains a little scribble of perplexity.

This child is the odd-man-out, and, pending the advent of her dazzling sister, is probably the most interesting; though nobody thinks so.

Little Céline, her dark eyes seeming huger and brighter because she is still only an infant, sits at the table, an open picture-book before her, but she is watching Pauline. A dimpled hand pushes up a plump round cheek.

How quiet it is. . . . She at the window has stopped knocking, hypnotised by the regularity of the falling snowflakes.

There they are in their quaint braided dresses, whose flounces seem to repeat the shapes of the valances and hangings, their neat kid boots, their staid propriety; such a commonplace little group, commonplace, yet with a difference. . . .

In the kitchen Louise, the cook, is stirring the good onion soup.

Upstairs Madame Martin is patiently waiting, her eyes on the crucifix on the wall before her.

The snow falls, and falls. . . .

Suddenly Léonie turns to exclaim:

"Here's papa coming!"

The street door opens, and Monsieur Martin enters hurriedly.

His cape is white-chested, and he bangs a glittering *aigrette* off his hat with his mittened hands as he turns on the step. His beard, too, is prematurely whitened.

There is an old woman with him, made anonymous by an enveloping cloak and hood.

They go upstairs together immediately.

After a little while Monsieur Martin comes down alone.

He is no longer quite so agitated, so we are able to see him more clearly as he stands cogitating, one hand on the blue glass ball of the banister.

He is an upright man of fifty, with an intellectual forehead, made more lofty by baldness. The eyes are quick and shrewd, though kindly. There is a certain mild hesitancy—is it a weakness?—behind his crisp, almost martial, bearing.

He goes into the kitchen to give some instruction to Louise, then joins his family in the parlor.

There is a lifting of heads when he comes in.

Marie pulls out his chair, Céline runs to fetch his beaded slippers.

Mamma is ill, but he tells them she will soon be better.

They resume their occupations, Monsieur Martin taking up a copy of *The Liturgical Year*, and deliberately sitting without crossing his legs. It is an occasion to mortify himself a little.

The air of formal obedience, somewhat constricting doubtless, does not stifle their spontaneity. They are still French, full of *esprit*. The room is really an aviary, the gestures and voices are those of twinkling domesticated birds.

Time passes. . . . Louise can be heard, brisk but heavy-footed, going up and down stairs. Between intervals of silence there are sounds and movements overhead, a dragged chair-castor squealing, a drawer bumped open, a water-can thumped down.

Silence . . . snow. . . .

Monsieur Martin turns over a page.

Suddenly another sound.

Is it a kitten mewing?

Monsieur Martin rises. A door bangs above. Louise descending. She knocks, opens, her brown Normandy face, with its little moustache, alight and smiling excitedly. She beckons her master.

In his haste Monsieur Martin bumps the table, and a blob of water splashes over on to Pauline's painting. That is very unlike papa!

Upstairs the old woman is swathing a red mouthing object in a white shawl.

It is another little girl.

And they had prayed so fervently that this time it would be a boy.

CHAPTER TWO

※

Death of a Mother

I

A SUNDAY AFTERNOON in summer, four years later.

The scene, a walled ring in another part of the town, with a vegetable plot, and at one side a hexagonal tower.

How comfortable it is in the purring sunshine. The "Zzz" of insects. Two yellow butterflies tumbling over each other above the cabbages. The sentinel sunflowers keeping out the world. Their heads have lolled over. They are asleep on their spears. The scent of sweet geranium in pots like upturned fezzes. The neat curling path of sand-crumbs. The scallop-shells of the border. The water in the lead tank dimpled by tap-drips. Plop—plop . . . the zoom of a fat bee . . . plop—plop . . . a sudden shrill of blackbird muted by thick leaves . . . plop—plop . . . a child's laughter, a grown-up's comment . . . and the heat like a glittering strawberry-net cast over everything.

This oasis is a small property acquired by Monsieur Martin from the profits of his clock and jewelry shop, before he retired to take over management of Zélie Guérin's lace business. He comes here, alone usually, to cultivate his garden, and meditate in the pavilion.

The lace of Alençon is manufactured in sections, each worker in a group specializing in one stitch. Madame Martin is a skilled "assembler," with several employees to whom she gives out the pricked patterns and orders. It was this way she earned her *dot,* it is said at the command of an interior voice.

She had wanted to become a Little Sister of the Poor. Louis had wanted to become a monk. But exemplary as were both their lives, they had neither of them, apparently, been granted

9

a religious vocation. Not, at any rate, in the sense they had hoped.

They met—previously they had been unaware of each other —and married almost immediately. It was like the story of Tobias and his spouse, who were joined in matrimony "solely for the love of children, in whom God's name might be blessed for ever and ever."

They longed for a son who would become a priest. Two sons had been born to them, but both had died in infancy. And now it was unlikely there would be any more.

Sitting against the warm wall, they are watching their five daughters.

They seem so complacent as to be almost irritating. Indeed, the whole legend of this family has been so carefully protected, so wrapped about with the thick veils of Sulpician piety, that it is almost impossible to penetrate, which is why we must allow ourselves complete freedom of imagination. It is the fear of scandal, which must always come, which has been responsible for turning these very real people into a kind of religious chessmen.

They were human, so they must have had frailties, but it can only be exciting if we accept the premises. They were middle-class, devout, in complete conformity to the will of God. Such an attitude is suspect now, but, as we hope to show, within such apparently rigid limitations it was possible to live fully, even adventurously.

The chief protagonist is so great, so authoritative, that her puissant truth will one day irradiate everything, dissolving the "bad taste," the "repression," the seeming "dullness" in a cloud of light. It is to her we must have recourse if we are to discover the secret.

At present she is scraping in the dirt like a little hen. The painted Italian watering-can almost hides her.

Prior to her birth her mother had been singing, and it had seemed to her that the child in her womb had sung back in answer. A propitious omen? She had thought so at the time, but at first it looked as though they would not be able to rear her.

The nuns at the Visitation Convent at Le Mans, including Sister Marie Dosithea, who was Madame Martin's sister, were requested to pray.

Then, when all seemed hopeless, a foster-mother, Rose Taillé, a buxom farmer's wife and herself the mother of several sturdy children, came to the rescue and took her to the country. They would go out to the village of Samallé to find the puny infant riding on the back of "Redskin" the cow.

She began to thrive.

"Get up out of the dirt immediately!" calls Madame Martin.

At first the child pretends not to hear, but before her mother has cause to raise her voice for the second time she comes out of her hole, clapping the earth off her tiny hands, smiling irresistibly. That smile, roguish, sweet, trustful yet private, is to become renowned.

She is quite plump. Her crisp low-cut skirt of *broderie anglaise* is like the frill of a daisy. There are the typical straight brows, but etched finer in her case. Her eyes are large and of a bluish-grey flecked with points of light, and her hair, drawn back by a ribbon, and hanging on to her puffed sleeves in conventional Sunday-ringlets, is golden like a doll's.

Dressed like a doll, even so the individuality breaks through. In repose the pretty little mouth is pressed determinedly. She has a disconcerting habit of looking one straight in the face. Stubborn, coquettish, proud, even a little petted perhaps, but there is no gainsaying her charm.

"Come and give me a kiss, little Queen," says Monsieur Martin, taking her on to his tight black knee, and she obediently puts her small saucy nose against his whiskers, as if to say: "I love you very much, but you shan't coerce me. I kiss you because you are my papa, and because you ask it."

"Her stubbornness is almost unconquerable," commented her

mother in a letter about this time. "When she has said 'No,' nothing will make her change; you might leave her all day in the cellar without getting her to say 'Yes.' She would rather sleep there than do so."

She was once offered a *sou* if she would mortify her self-love by kissing the ground, but, to quote her own words written seventeen years later: ". . . my pride was up in arms, and, holding myself erect, I replied: "No, thank you, mamma, I would rather go without the *sou'*."

It was probably no more than a form of self-respect, a kind of positive love of self without which love for one's neighbor would be meaningless—selfishness, negative self-love, belonging to a quite different category.

She was always remorseful when she could not obey at once, but it was necessary to realize herself first. Obedience, yes, but not blind obedience. Later love itself would take such complete possession of her that the effort to obey would be of secondary importance, but there would be jagged mountains to climb, arid deserts to cross, before she would arrive at that place of bliss.

In God's time, to use her own metaphor drawn from the latest invention of her age—the contemporaneity of the image is a sign of her originality, she seldom used hackneyed phraseology, except in her conventional poetry—she would rise as in a lift. Fallen nature would continue to present difficulties, and there would be spiritual ones of an inconceivable horror; even so, the lift, God's arms, would carry her up in spite of her sufferings. But it would not be yet.

As much as she enjoyed showing-off, feeling most disappointed when she was not allowed to pay a visit with bare arms —"I should have looked much prettier"—there was already a latent desire to be hidden.

"I don't want anyone to look at me," she whimpered when Marie and Madame Martin turned back the bed-clothes one morning to give her a kiss.

And the rational French mind, the remorseless logic which was to prove such a source of irritation—for which they would later be grateful—to her novices, was already even now displaying itself in the wish that her parents would die quickly so as to go to Heaven!

When Léonie, who was getting too big for toys, came and offered a basket of playthings to her two younger sisters, Céline chose a woollen ball, but Thérèse had no hesitation in snatching the lot!

"I choose everything!" she exclaimed, and so she did, including the deaths of the martyrs. The toys were merely types of the future pangs she would hug with such supernatural jealousy. So great, so infinite, would be her heart's desire for assuagement that she would cry out with an almost divine folly "to be scourged, crucified, flayed alive like St. Bartholomew, plunged in boiling oil like St. John, ground by the teeth of wild beasts like St. Ignatius of Antioch."

In the eyes of the world this may sound like madness, but the pathological aspect of pain, the little *cul-de-sac* labelled masochism, is quite off the track of that tremendous comet-sweep of the soul's trajectory which knows that the highest form of love, that point of ecstatic incandescence when its being is consumed, is one with its Maker, can only be arrived at through the extravagances of sacrifice.

It was her affectionate nature, her overwhelming desire to love and to be loved, that was successful in mitigating her small egotistical failings.

She was especially fond of Céline. To use her own simile, they were like twin flowers blooming on one stem, like the two bantams their nurse had given them, impossible to imagine separated.

Her confidence in love, even at this early age—but what more natural than to trust love when a child?—her Little Way, the new system for the direction of souls for which she was to become so celebrated, was derived from this—her confidence in love was extreme. She felt she could escape from hell itself by flinging herself into the arms of her mother.

And because she was so fair among her darker sisters, so outstandingly personable, the "Little Benjamin," her parents can hardly be blamed if they seemed to make a favorite of her. If they had spoiled her—which they did not—she would have said she had been spared the consequences entirely through grace.

She did realize afterwards she had been in danger, and that the danger would have been worse had she not been given "a father and mother worthier of Heaven than of Earth."

She thought she might have become like Mary Magdalen, regretted its not being so to some extent, for then God's magnanimity would have had more to forgive. Pious she most certainly was, but there was nothing "holier than thou" about her.

She dreamed of goblins, prancing in irons on a lime barrel in the garden like an illustration to the brothers Grimm, but it was the goblins, not the child, who were afraid. It was her first premonition of evil, and it left her undismayed.

Perhaps she would be vouchsafed a consoling memory of that during the almost annihilating struggle that lay a little way ahead—and in that other terrible bout towards the end, whose long-drawn-out torments would be indescribable, seeming to have passed the dimensions of this life and entered into the eternity of damnation—perhaps, but so that her abandonment should be as complete as her Beloved's, perhaps not. . . .

But it is still summer in the secret garden. She is not yet five years old. Idyllic days when unhappiness was no more than having to go early to bed . . .

2

Madame Martin rises, and collects her brood.

Marie is getting quite grown-up, remembers to walk with

circumspect correctness, her rich dark hair coiled into a low bun. Pauline, poor darling, is not yet emerged from the adolescent chrysalis. Monsieur Guérin, her uncle, who is a chemist at Lisieux, has sent a bottle of flowers of sulphur, so her pinkness is dashed with mealy yellow as if she had brushed through pollen. Léonie has been quite good today. Perhaps the Holy Water they have rubbed on her brow has taken effect?

Céline grasps Thérèse firmly by the hand, and they go twinkling ahead.

Papa will follow later. He is going to meddle with his collection of flies, read a little in his eyrie at the top of the tower.

And what of Madame Martin herself?

As she shepherds them out of the gate, just before she takes Marie's arm, a sharp spasm—or is it merely a sudden dipping bough of shadow?—causes her to wince. But before anyone can remark it, she calls out some instruction about crossing the road, is smiling again.

3

But it had been more than a passing shadow. Within a few weeks Madame Martin was dead.

The disease has been attributed to a knock against the corner of a table, but whatever the starting point it would seem that little was done to arrest its progress. Her brother, the chemist, was consulted; there was even some talk of an operation, but for some reason or other it was put off. Perhaps it was greatly her own fault, for she was adept at hiding a women's ailments. A pilgrimage to Lourdes was suddenly embarked on, where she resolutely cast her wracked body into the icy waters, but, in her case, their healing properties were of no avail.

She returned home to go to bed—that bed in which she had submitted at last. The first year of the Martins' marriage had been spent in a brother-and-sisterly chastity, then, just as deliberately, we are told—though it is unlikely it was quite so detached—the position was modified in order to raise a family for the glory of God.

That bed stands today in the little memorial church built on the house at Alençon. Indeed, the actual bedroom forms a side chapel. And it does not appear incongruous.

There are the same blue and yellow brocade hangings, out of which the young Thérèse formed a tent in which to meditate. Her high chair stands at one side. And on the wall her christening robes, like diaphanous linen butterflies, are pinned in a glass case.

Madame Martin's resistance was beginning to ebb. She who, during the strictly observed Lenten fasts, had found the weight of her dress wellnigh insupportable, was about to slip off the weight of the flesh.

The priest came to administer Extreme Unction.

The children, with Monsieur Martin, knelt round the bed.

Many years after, in Carmel, Thérèse could still see the lace valance where she had got down, could still hear her father's sobs.

The conventional appurtenances of death in a French provincial household can be very tasteless, but there was no question, apparently, of disguising anything in order to protect the delicate psyche of a little girl.

Later, when her mother's agony was over, Monsieur Martin took her to kiss her goodbye. Sentimentalists will insist that death is like sleep. It is not always so. The soul has gone, and without a soul a body may have a strange look.

It must have been terrifying for a child of five years to have been brought so solemnly into the presence of that mystery. The bogey-shadows from the tall candles on the walls of the shuttered room . . . the rigid effigy, with its feet erect under the counterpane like the cold peaks of mountains, the stark head, its brow polished and luminous as yellow marble, its stony weight pressing so deep into the pillows—deeper than in sleep—and the unnaturally crossed hands, from whose stiff fingers depended mournful ivy-trails . . . what possible connection could all these waxwork trappings have with her mamma? —she who had bent over her in her cot like a sweet-scented cloud of summer, she whose reliable arms had always been ready to lift her up out of trouble, whose whispering kiss had soothed away all her fears—she who had been alive . . . ?

No wonder Thérèse was unable to speak. The shock so numbed her she was scarcely able to cry.

This repression of grief was to have distressing repercussions.

When the coffin arrived a morbid compulsion made her go and look at it, leaning against the wall on the landing. It was so tall in comparison to herself, "a huge and melancholy thing," that she had to raise her head to encompass it.

After the funeral the five girls were sitting in the parlor with their nurse, a woman for whom most likely births, marriages, and burials had a not unpleasurable importance. At any rate, she seems to have been determined to squeeze out the last drop of pathos.

We can almost see the shaking of her black-bonneted head, hear her histrionic sigh, as, eyeing them lugubriously, she reminded, with what tactless superfluity: "Poor little things, you have no longer a mother!"

Céline flung herself into the arms of Marie.

"You shall be my mother!" she exclaimed.

Thérèse, whose instinct was to imitate Céline in everything, was about to follow suit, when she suddenly decided it might make Pauline feel neglected (no one seems to have given a thought to Léonie) and, instead, offered herself to that sister.

It was a happy choice, as we shall see.

❦

CHAPTER THREE

In the Doll's-house

I

LISIEUX—EVOCATIVE, THE center of millions of devotions, the calyx of the mystical rose. But it does not look it.

We have descended into a black peasant world, dour, clenched, and unprepossessing. Pot-holes, rubble; row upon row of cabin-like structures serving as temporary shops and dwelling-places.

The gigantic new basilica, its modern-Byzantine domes emerging from their scaffolding like a collection of spinning-tops, dominates what is left of the town from the top of the hill.

By a miracle the Carmel remains intact after the war, as does the house Les Buissonnets, and the ancient Gothic church of St. Pierre, its asymmetrical towers standing like two old burgesses on the platform of steps above the market-place. The Benedictine school of Notre Dame du Pré, where the saint was educated, vanished one night—just like that. The remains of the Church of St. Jacques are like the ribs of some weird sea-monster washed inland æons of years ago, and seemingly unearthed by the terrible bombardment. They have already built a new church behind it in the form of a concrete boot-box.

The ubiquitous jangle-hung *palais des rosaires*—these and the dingy cafés, being the main sources of livelihood—importune incessantly. They are like the rain.

It is so damp joints and hinges creak in concert. A tarpaulin sky hangs down behind the skeletons of houses. The water-logged air vibrates to an orchestra of continual clinking and knocking as if they were beating cans with bones.

And they say that this town was once pretty, with narrow upward-winding streets of beamed and gabled dwellings nodding to one another across the cobbles like gossiping Normandy head-dresses. . . .

The House of the Salamander, its lintels a grotesque bestiary, remains as an example.

It must have looked like that when the Martins arrived, a mediæval curiosity to be walked past and peered at by the occupants of the proper nineteenth-century villas of the more respectable quarter.

Les Buissonnets, The Bushes—were they burning bushes? —stands at the top of a labyrinth of lanes, beyond whose fences nod, for it is autumn, the shaggy suns of dahlias. Pumpkins have been set out to ripen on steps. An old gardener in a hood of sack is stringing up onions on the door of a shed.

This way—we are nearly at the top—now we can see the steep sloping mansard of the doll's-house peering smugly above the privacy of its high wall.

Within the gates we are in a little world; the intimate world of the French bourgeoisie, whose laws are easier to define than those of the planets, but are no less undeviating.

There is a time and a place for everything here, everything mentionable, that is. Prudence is the ruling virtue, the proprieties her subjects. It is quaint, absurd, exasperating, yet not without a curious attraction.

The Martins have come so as to be near their relatives, the Guérins. Madame Guérin, who has two daughters herself, Jeanne and Marie, will be able to advise Monsieur Martin on the upbringing of his own girls.

Yes, it is a doll's-house, its little parlors, bedrooms, peaked attics, and garden seemingly as safe as that. The walls are red brick with white facing-stones, and a narrow lead border, like the paper-lace inside old-fashioned chocolate-boxes, is attached to the sloping sides of the mansard and gables.

It is all part of a convention.

But life refuses to be insulated by knives and forks, tables and chairs. A decision of great importance will be arrived at here. Something rather more momentous than the choosing of stuffs for curtains or dresses, the arranging of the menu for a little dinner-party, whether to plant aubrietia or calceolarias in the half-moon *parterres*. Meanwhile that is the way we must live for a season, and if we choose to adapt ourselves it need not prove uninteresting.

The sedate villa set in its small neat grounds is just the same today as it was then, except that it has been turned into a reliquary, the toy-box of a saint.

Here we may see, even handle, if the sister-in-charge is disposed to draw back the glass shutters, her own bed, her doll and doll's bed, her school-books and satchel, doll's tea-set, a kaleidoscope, a boat, a miniature fishing-basket, a draught-board, a tiny piano with five notes, a top, an oven, a skipping-rope, and her childhood jewels, including a gold cross, the first Communion watch, a brilliant and a filigree brooch like a butterfly, a bracelet, and a tiny pair of silver-gilt earrings.

2

We could paint four pictures from the past, the four seasons. . . .

The front lawn, with its two stone urns, is framed by an oval drive, The garden at the back is raised, and divided into two parts. Little paths twine in and out among shrubbery. There is a wash-house and an arbor. The trees are Scotch firs, and there is an elderberry and an apple. A swing dangles.

In autumn bloodstreak sunsets stain the sky on the level of the attics. The town can just be seen in its lake of mist below scrabbles of frail branches.

Then will come the furry snow-cloaks, the needle-fans will be heavy and creaking, the only faint sound in the thick silence of winter, and a little scarlet figure will run out to throw crumbs for the dejected birds.

In spring the chirping new green will spark on tips and grassplots, the daffodil bell ringing to announce an unending procession of flowers.

And in summer the buzzing perfumed air will be badged and brooched with roses. . . .

Her world will always be a garden, even when she is shut away behind the black grille. Carmel, too, is a garden, one in which she will gather many bitter herbs, but there will be other flowers of an unimaginable loveliness, rare spiritual blossoms inconceivable to the grossness of the senses . . . but still not yet.

Life resumed its even tenor, broken now and again by holidays at the sea with their cousins. They would go to Trouville, made fashionable by the departed Empress. Her ghost, surrounded by her ladies, as in a picture by Boudin, might have been seen treading the level sands, a frieze of delicate-stepping birds against the aquamarine background, their fringed sunshades replicas of the jewel-bright seaanemones. . . .

But a change had taken place in Thérèse. No longer sunny and carefree, she suffered from headaches, was peevish, fractious, ready at the slightest provocation to burst into tears.

It was at about this time she was vouchsafed a mysterious vision. We will let her describe it in her own words:

". . . Papa was away from home and was not expected back till late. It would be about two or three o'clock in the afternoon; the sun shone brightly and all Nature seemed at play. I was alone at a window which looked out on the large kitchen garden, my mind full of pleasant thoughts, when I saw, in front of the wash-house opposite, a man dressed exactly like Papa, and of the same height and demeanor, though more bent and aged. I say *aged*, to convey an idea of his general appearance, because, the head being covered with a thick veil, I did not see his face. Slowly and with measured steps he advanced, and passed by my own little garden. Overcome by a feeling of supernatural dread I called out loudly and in frightened tones: 'Papa, Papa!' The mysterious person seemed not to hear, and continued on his way without even turning round, went towards a clump of fir-trees which divided in two the garden walk. I expected him to reappear behind the tall firs, but the prophetic vision had vanished.

"It was all over in a moment, but it was a moment which impressed itself so deeply upon me that even now, after so many years, the memory of it stands out as distinct as the vision itself.

"You (Pauline) and Marie were in an adjoining room, and at my cry of 'Papa!' you were both seized with fear. Concealing her emotion, Marie ran to me, saying: 'Why do you call Papa like that when he is at Alençon?' I described what I had just seen, and to reassure me I was told that the maid must have covered her head with her apron on purpose to frighten me.

"When questioned, however, Victoire (another servant) declared that she had not left the kitchen, and besides, the truth was deeply engraved on my mind; I had seen a man, and that man was exactly like Papa. Together we went to look behind the fir-trees, and, finding nothing, you told me to think no more about it. But to banish the thought was impossible. Often and often this mysterious vision rose up before me. Often and often I tried to lift the veil which hid its true meaning, and deep down in my heart lay the conviction that some day it would be fully revealed."

She was right. But its interpretation would not be made clear to her until the arrival of the event it had presaged.

Meanwhile she did her best to be good, to try and endure, without inflicting her misery on others, the exacerbating and irrational sensitivity which had descended on her like a cloak of barbs.

There were moments of lightness. Her walks with the father she adored—she would sit and watch him fishing, lost in a haze of poignant, melancholy thoughts which, even at that early age, were sometimes transcendental, and there was an occasion, clutching his hand tightly on their way home in the dusk, when she thought she saw her name written in the heavens. It was the letter T in the constellation Orion.

There would be cosy Sunday evenings visiting her uncle and aunt in the other part of the town. Monsieur Guérin would take her on his knee and sing the "Song of Bluebeard," which she found deliciously frightening.

By now she was eight years of age; her schooling was in progress at the Benedictine Convent, where, as was not very surprising, she was bullied and misunderstood by her class-mates; but she told no one of this, sustaining herself with the consolation of knowing she would find comfort when she got home. Surrounded by the members of her family, she felt safe and protected.

Then in 1882 Pauline was received into Carmel.

For Thérèse it was a dreadful shock. It was like losing her mother over again.

She wanted to go with her, and this so human longing was the beginning of her own vocation. She was taken to see Mother Marie Gonzague, the Reverend Mother.

The dark cloth covering the grille in the convent parlor was raised, a privilege granted only to near relatives, intending postulants, and young children, and she was able to speak of her desires face to face. The nun believed her to be sincere, but told her she would have to wait until she was at least sixteen, as it was not the custom to receive postulants at the age of nine!

The delicately adjusted young organism was now strained to breaking point.

The sight of her sister behind those cruel bars, clad in the dowdy unfamiliar dress of a novice, black ankle-length skimpy gown and comic bonnet, unable to caress her any more, and to whom she could say practically nothing because of her uncontrollable grief—visitors were only allowed half an hour, and

naturally Monsieur Martin and Marie took the largest share—
was more than she could bear.

She became terribly ill.

Her tortured state was even more distressing because nobody
seemed to be able to do anything to relieve it. It was as if she
were shut away alone into a glass-walled world of terror. Her
loved ones moved about outside, gesturing to her, tenderly concerned, solicitous, bewildered and impotent.

As in so many nervous illnesses a perverse refusal on her
own part seemed to forbid her to tell them what was wrong.
She banged her head in a frenzy of desperation against the bed-
board. Sometimes a mysterious thrusting force pushed her out
on to the floor. She felt she was suspended over bottomless
precipices; the nails in the wall on which her gentle childhood
pictures were hung turned into witch-like admonishing fingers;
once, when her father stood watching her in silence, the hat in
his hand was metamorphosed into some indescribably disgust-
ing shape, causing her to toss away shrieking and sobbing.

She recovered sufficiently to be able to attend her sister's
clothing, but immediately the ceremony was over the wild hurl-
ing paroxysms returned with an added violence. She was deranged. They feared she would go completely mad, or die of
exhaustion in her unavailing attempts to do combat with these
gusts and winds from the abyss. It was surely the devil himself
pitting the whole force of the powers of darkness against this
simple innocent child in whom he had recognized a potentially
triumphant adversary.

A novena was begun for her at the shrine of Our Lady of
Victories in Paris.

On the last day Léonie and Marie were watching by her bed.
The latter got up to go and exercise herself for a few minutes
in the garden. Then . . . but we will let the saint tell us what
happened for herself:

"After a while I began to call in a low voice: 'Marie, Marie!'
Accustomed to hear me fret in this way, Léonie took no notice,
so I called out louder and Marie came back to me. I distinctly

saw her enter, but for the first time I failed to recognize her. I looked piteously round the room and towards the garden, crying again and again: 'Marie, Marie!' Words cannot convey the agony of that moment, and Marie's suffering was perhaps greater than mine. At last, after many fruitless efforts to make me recognize her, she whispered to Léonie and went away pale and trembling.

"A few minutes later Léonie carried me to the window overlooking the garden, where I could see Marie walking slowly up and down. She held out her arms to me with a smile, and called tenderly: 'Thérèse, my little Thérèse!' but still I did not know her. This last effort failing, she returned to my room and knelt in tears at the foot of the bed. Then, looking towards the statue, she implored Our Lady's assistance with all the fevor of a mother who begs the life of her child and will not be refused. Léonie and Céline joined in her prayers, and that cry of faith forced the gates of Heaven.

"Utterly exhausted, and finding no help on earth, I too sought my heavenly mother's aid, and entreated her with all my heart to have pity on me.

"Suddenly the statue became animated and radiantly beautiful—with a divine beauty which no words of mine can ever convey. The look upon Our Lady's face was unspeakably kind and sweet and compassionate, but what penetrated to the very depths of my soul was her gracious smile. Instantly all my pain vanished, my eyes filled, and big tears fell silently, tears of purest heavenly joy."

She was cured.

But the favor carried with it a curious anticlimax. She felt that if she confirmed the miracle—her sisters could not fail to notice that the Virgin had granted her some extraordinary grace —she would lose her precious regained happiness.

Marie persuaded her, and she admitted what had happened.

Immediately the light went out.

For four years she could not think of her cure without a feeling of acute self-repugnance.

✼

CHAPTER FOUR

A Chain of Fly-papers

I

THAT ILLNESS HAD been a dissonant crescendo, and one might have thought that the notes following it would have been harmonious and full of peace. But it was not so. The final passage of the movement, which we could call Childhood, was, certainly, to echo with a pæan of praise, but in its approach to that sun-burst the music was to follow a melancholy and at times tortuous path, albeit relieved by transitory moments of prophetic gaiety and happiness.

In this lull we may pause to look again at the instrument. She is beginning to grow taller, is passing into that rather disquieting period between the prettiness of infancy and the bloom of early girlhood. The face is thinner, enormous with eyes, and the body slender and responsive as a spear of trembling-grass. No longer exciting the sentimental endearments grown-ups shower on—as they might have said—a cuddlesome morsel of babyhood, she is beginning to be regarded with a more sensuous, a more adult appreciation.

At this time, probably to divert her and thus prevent a lapse into her recent dangerous introspection, her father takes her about. On the front at the sea-side, in the more familiar streets and drawing-rooms of her home-town, admiring speculative glances are cast on this pale gravely smiling creature, who moves with the dignified gait of a princess under her great burden of golden hair.

Compliments are passed. She is made to feel a person of coming importance. But solitude is not the prerogative of the unprepossessing. Like certain other strange and glamorous

26

characters, whom one feels have only to put out a finger to draw towards them the whole world, she is mysteriously lonely.

Human relationships do not go right for her. She does not succeed in winning friendship among her schoolgirl associates, any more than in attracting the favoritism of her teachers. Her companions are pictures and books, and of course God.

Later, perhaps even then, for she was precociously logical, she was to attribute this denial to protective grace. God wanted her for himself alone, and it was only in him she would be able to love everybody.

The time draws near for her first Communion. Marie has prepared her for three months, though she had prepared herself with innumerable tiny sacrifices, flowers, she called them, since the occasion of Céline's first Communion four years ago.

The last days are spent in making a retreat at the Abbey, not coming home, but sleeping in a cubicle in the long dormitory watched over by the devoted dames. She walks about in a state of ecstatic anticipation, an enormous crucifix, such as missionaries wore, tucked into her belt—no wonder her companions found her rather odd!

What a little prig she might have turned into, but her simplicity and directness, her extraordinary innocence, saved her. Her purity must have been luminous. Not a very fashionable virtue these days, and, indeed, there is no need to stress it, for no virtue of itself, except perhaps charity, has ever been a passport to sanctity, a fact of which she was only too well aware.

She knew she had been fortunate in her upbringing, in the way her first father—her Heavenly Father—had given her such exemplary parents on earth, for without that initial training a creature as passionate and temperamental as she was might have become—what?

"Our Lord has forgiven me even more than He forgave St. Mary Magdalen," she said, likening His goodness to that of a thoughtful parent who, instead of binding up the sore place of his child who has stumbled over a stone, anticipates the mishap by removing the obstacle before it can happen.

As well as being grateful it exasperated her a little, as it meant she must give the lie to those who claimed that an innocent soul has never loved more than a repentant one. But this apparently favored condition worked out well. Never, never would she set herself up, and her burning compassion for those who had been tempted and fallen was already, as we shall see later, about to manifest itself.

At last the long-awaited morning arrived.

Pauline, now Sister Agnes of Jesus, was about to go to the altar in Carmel, not for Her Lord to give Himself to her, but so that she might offer herself to Him. It was to be the day of her divine espousals. The two sisters must have had each other very much in mind.

Thérèse called this day the most beautiful of her life. We can imagine her appearance, lily-white and shining, in a veil and dress of snow, her ringleted gold crowned with rose, and we can watch her with the other awed little girls, moving up to the rails, with dangling rosaries of pearl or crystal, their palms pressed together devoutly, their wonder-bearing eyes hidden in lowered glances, but beyond that point we dare not venture.

She said herself: ". . . I would not and I could not tell you all. Some things lose their fragrance when exposed to the air." So we will not presume to obtrude on the mysterious communings between a little child and Almighty God. Enough to say they "were no longer two. Thérèse had disappeared like a drop of water lost in the immensity of the ocean: Jesus alone remained—He was the Master, the King." The liberty which had frightened her so much had gone for ever.

They took her, moving as in a dream, to see Pauline, dressed like herself in a white veil and a wreath of roses.

At home there was a feast, and her father gave her a watch.

She went to bed in a state of tranquil joy.

The morrow dawned on unaccountable feelings of emptiness and flatness already the *accidia* of the world.

2

It is a curious fact, but prior to all the important events in Thérèse's life to which she looked forward there was a delay.

For instance, had she been born a few days earlier she would have made her first Communion in the previous year, and now, for some reason which has not been made clear, the ceremony of Confirmation was postponed.

But it came eventually. The Holy Ghost filled her with such supernatural ardor that, speaking to Céline of what this Sacrament meant to her, the latter was so overawed by her young sister's expression, which seemed momentarily to have become like that of an angel of light, that she could not endure it, and, lowering her eyes, made some excuse to leave the room.

There was no doubt divine providence would have its way with this chosen soul no matter what happened.

But the flames of her Joan-of-Arc-like zeal were not yet powerful enough to burn away all dross in a flash. The process was slow and painful, excrutiating so. She suddenly fell a victim to that miserable spiritual disease of scruples.

To one who has never suffered from this distressing complaint its symptoms might well appear absurd. It is said that the germ is pride, and that it incubates with most success in perfectionist natures. The sensitive highly-strung organism of the young Thérèse, excessively overbred in religious sensibilities, was the perfect breeding ground. The good strong Normandy common-sense, of which at bottom she had an abundance, was powerless to come to the rescue. For two years she was unable to free herself. It was like struggling in bands of fly-paper. No sooner would she succeed in detaching, so to speak, an arm, than a leg would be caught, and so on, and so on, continuously in a seemingly endless, conflict.

The most harmless actions assumed the dread significance of mortal sins. She could not wear a hair-ribbon her aunt had given her without going immediately to confess her vanity. She cried continually, and was ashamed. The convolutions were inextricable. She began to cry for having cried!

Her behavior was becoming such a source of embarrassment that Monsieur Martin had to take her away from the Benedictine school and have her education continued privately.

Another holiday at Trouville with the Guérins did little to help. Indeed, it made her worse. Noticing how, when her cousin Marie complained of a headache she was immediately fondled and sympathized with, Thérèse resolved to become an exhibitionist herself. She wanted so desperately to be understood. Later she was not to care what anybody thought, but at this stage the human side asserted itself. Why not? She was only thirteen years old, motherless, hypersensitive, even a little neurotic, it seems.

It was right she should suffer these things. They were to make her humble, understanding, detached, and truly compassionate. But in the thick of the battle she was not conscious of the outcome. How could she be?

Imitating little Marie, she flung herself into a chair and acted (she could have been a great actress, perhaps . . .) the part of the neglected waif.

"My head aches!" she moaned.

She really did have headaches, but previously she had kept quiet about them.

But her performance was not appreciated. All she got for her pains was to be accused of a lack of simplicity.

Sometimes by confiding her fantastic and extravagant thoughts to Marie, her sister, she was able to obtain a temporary relief. But it was only temporary. The next day she would be just as hopelessly entangled.

She tried to win commendation by helping with menial tasks in the house, such as making her own bed, fetching and carrying, looking after Céline's plants and cuttings when she was not there, but if her good deeds passed unnoticed she was disproportionately, ridiculously hurt, and the ever-ready tears started again. Any real faults she had were increased by her cloying morbid remorse. She must have seemed impossible!

In October 1886 her sister Marie joined Pauline in Carmel, so that Thérèse was now bereft of her "third mother."

Léonie, certainly kind at heart, was silently preoccupied with her own peculiar problems, which we will refer to later. Thérèse and Céline were drawn even closer, but they were both little more than children, and the elder had usually appealed to the younger for advice. Perhaps, she imagined, she was a little out of favor with Papa?

It was now she had the idea of enlisting the aid of the "holy innocents," her four young brothers and sisters who had died in infancy. She spoke to them as simply as if they were with her on the earth, grown-up now, and protecting. She asked them to intercede for her peace.

And on Christmas Eve her prayer was answered.

She was to refer to it as the end of the "second period."

3

Christmas Eve in Normandy. . . .

Sabots or silken slippers arranged in pairs on the hearths of cabins or chateaux. Tonight that old haw-cheeked pagan, Santa Claus, is whipping his reindeers over the roof-tops . . . sleigh-bells, church-bells. . . . The Child Jesus is coming again to be born in the frost and straw.

The animals kneel in the manger, their breaths curling like incense. Above the hills an invisible choir is singing.

The great star, a rose of ice in the blue shines out across the sleeping darkness of the world. . . .

The three Martin girls and their father have just returned from Midnight Mass.

Victoire has made up the fire only a few minutes before their arrival, so the yule log—a concession to the festive occasion—little ivy-leaves still twined about its gnarled sides, splutters, and puffs, and sparks across the iron dogs.

Léonie, still wearing her sealskin pill-box, brings out the thick white breakfast-cups for hot chocolate.

Monsieur Martin, indulging himself for once, is rubbing his stiff fingers over the snapping flames.

There is only one pair of shoes in the hearth tonight, their slender cavities piled with intriguing-looking packages.

Céline and Thérèse, having flown upstairs to put away their coats and hats, are about to fly down again for the ceremony.

Monsieur Martin—perhaps he is a little piqued by the east wind (how it howls in the chimney! . . .)—thinking they are out of ear-shot, says somewhat irritably to Léonie: "All this is far too babyish for a big girl like Thérèse, and I hope this is the last time it will happen."

On the staircase above, the two girls pause and look at each other.

The sharp unwitting blow has brought the tears to Thérèse's eyes once more. Not another crying fit, surely, not on Christfas Eve?

Céline drags at her sister's arm.

"Don't go down just yet, you would only give way if you looked at your presents before Papa."

But, no—casting off in one quick gesture of heroic virtue every vestige of pride and self-love—she is down on the hearth, unwrapping her gifts with an hilarious simulated happiness which has suddenly become real.

Her self-consciousness is over for ever!

In the words of the psalmist, from this moment she begins "to run as a giant."

CHAPTER FIVE

※

"A Time of Lovers"

I

THE SCRAWNY AWKWARD days have gone the way of battered satchels and scratched pencil-cases. She begins to grow in grace and beauty.

The heart beats faster, mantling the cheeks with rose-leaf blushes, her hair, eyes, the whole outline, taking on a sheen and a fragrance as of some exquisite bird or flower. All created things, the plants, the animals, her fellow creatures, are awakening a response in her.

She sits at the window of the roof garden in the palpitating nights of spring, the warm still nights of summer, sometimes alone, more often with her devoted Céline, where, entwined like two Rossetti virgins, they are counting the stars in the heavens, the stars in their own veins.

Their talk was poetically metaphysical, their emotions rapt and religious.

> "Treading in Thy footsteps
> Young maidens lightly run upon the way,
> From the spark's contact,
> And the spiced wine.
> They give forth aspirations of a balm divine."

So does a quotation from St. John of the Cross, one of her favorite authors, describe them aptly.

In the words of Thérèse herself:

"Doubt would have been impossible; already faith and hope were passing from our souls; love was bringing us here below to Him we sought."

The house is full of pets. Doves, parrots, canaries, bull-

finches, linnets flutter through her days like the darting cor-
ruscations of her dreams. Goldfishes bend and flash in a glass
bowl. Their father brings home a new-born lamb, but, alas, it
dies, as do the silkworms from a lack of mulberry leaves, and
are buried in "the kingdom of the moles." But she has a consoling spaniel, called Tom, who receives her prodigal caresses
and thrives on them.

Another girl would doubtless have begun to have inclina-
tions towards the opposite sex, probably as yet no more than
sentimental speculations, day-dreams begot of novels and gossip
with *confidantes,* but it would have been in that direction, quite
naturally, that her expectations of fulfilment would have
tended.

In Thérèse's case it was different. She was falling in love
with God.

Nevertheless, at this period, she was drawn towards a man.

An odd specimen, it must be admitted. Neither a fictitious
youth compounded of her readings of the lives of chivalrous
heroes, nor one of the proper, dullish eligible young men of
the Lisieux community, but a notorious fascinator of the under-
world, a creature about to be guillotined for a series of brutal
murders. A strange choice, surely, for such a carefully brought-
up young lady of the bourgeoisie, nurtured on piety, and protected from shocking reality by the garden-wall of the conventions? Perhaps. . . .

2

For a moment we must turn to Léonie.

She has been drawing attention to herself for some time,
disturbing the tranquil background of the *ménage* by her knocks
and tuts and rattlings, and other jarring manifestations of a
clumsy susceptibility.

Nobody seems to have known quite what was the matter
with Léonie. She was the third child, and the previous offspring had also been girls. Maybe she had overheard her parents

expressing their disappointment that she was not the son they had longed for, and that involuntary slight, like an unextracted splinter, had remained to rankle in her affections? Perhaps she found the pious examples of her sisters, which were, to say the least of it, rather exceptional, too difficult to live up to? She may have been jealous of the adulated baby Thérèse? We do not know.

That she had a strenuously persevering character there is no doubt, for she entered the religious life and succeeded in remaining in it after three attempts. In the convent where she died they invoke her as a saint.

It has been suggested that, misunderstood by her parents, she came under the domination of a crude-natured servant who, for the satisfaction of wielding power over another, encouraged the child to be naughty. Again we cannot be certain.

That Madame Martin, who in other respects was apparently the acme of understanding and kindliness, seems to have, in the case of this one daughter, allowed her zeal for the good life to have got the better of her wisdom is demonstrated in the harsh way poor Léonie was corrected.

A story was recounted to her of a little girl whose unconfessed sin crawled out of her mouth in the form of a serpent. She was also given a set of counters with the instruction that every time she made a little sacrifice she was to place one of the tallies in a special drawer. It is hardly surprising—indeed it probably speaks well for Léonie's innate healthy-mindedness —that at the end of the week when the drawer was opened it was found to be empty.

But now she is twenty-four. Pauline and Marie have been drawn undeviatingly by the lodestar of Carmel. Céline and Thérèse are wrapped up in each other and their mystical communings. Monsieur Martin, who has had a slight stroke, and who perhaps was never entirely sympathetic to her, is even less communicative.

Was it her desire to be loved, to be part of a community, to be no longer left out of things, to escape somehow from the criticism, real or imagined, of her disapproving relations? She may even have taken fright at the thought that her father's illness would become progressive, and that she would find herself a prisoner with the task of nursing for untold years, a circumstance which was eventually to materialize.

Whatever the human reasons, it was, despite its immediate failure, a true religious vocation which was compelling her, but it would take a baptism of fire to prove it. Suddenly, then, on an imprudent impulse, as the know-alls were to remark when she came out again, Léonie got herself admitted to the Visitation Convent at Caen. The nervous tension in the household must have been considerably eased by her departure.

3

Thérèse and Céline could now share the secrets of grace in undisturbed intimacy.

It was as it said in the prophecies of Ezechial: "Behold thy time was the time of lovers: and I spread my garments over thee. And I swore to thee, and I entered into a covenant with thee, saith the Lord God, and thou becamest Mine. And I washed thee with water and I anointed thee with oil. I clothed thee with fine garments, and put a chain about thy neck. Thou didst eat fine flour and honey and oil, and wast made exceedingly beautiful, and wast advanced to be a queen."

One Sunday, at the end of Mass, a picture of the Crucifixion protruded as Thérèse shut her missal, and she saw the pierced hand of Jesus dripping the precious Blood with, seemingly, no one to gather it up. His cry "I thirst!" echoed in herself, and she felt an unslakable desire to save sinners. She would stand at the foot of the cross, and collect the Blood, and offer it back to God to redeem the souls of the lost.

At about this time the front pages of French newspapers

were stamped across with the sensational headlines of the Pranzini murders.

Perhaps Thérèse had come across her information in the kitchen, for it was unlikely that those black-smeared sheets, reeking of lust and worldliness, would have been discovered among the flowers and paint-brushes of the doll's-house drawing-room.

At any rate, somehow or other, the plight of the murderer, cynical and remorseless, about to be executed in what seemed like a state of damnation, got itself brought to the notice of her eager charity. There was no question of disgust, or of being frightened and thrilled by his sadistic activities. Thérèse saw only a haggard blundering soul about to shut itself out from the love of God for ever.

She prayed.

"My God, I am sure Thou wilt pardon this unhappy Pranzini, and I shall still think so even if he does not confess his sins or give any sign of sorrow—such is the confidence I have in Thy unbounded mercy. But because this is my first sinner, I beg for just one *sign* of repentance to reassure me."

On the morning of the execution, at the risk of incurring her father's anger, she obtained a copy of *La Croix*.

Her heart sprang as she read the last words of the brief account.

At the final moment, just before being strapped to the machine, Pranzini had reached out for the crucifix in the hands of the attendant priest, and kissed it three times.

Often, later, in Carmel, she had masses said for the repose of the soul of this her "first child."

"I must not forget him," she would say, adding quite simply, "he must need it after having played so many pranks."

We perhaps find it difficult to condone murder, especially murder with cruelty, piling upon the unfortunates who perpetrate it that great weight of guilt and retribution which we feel, in the disguise of moral indignation, for our own terrible, or ridiculous, uncommitted crimes.

But Thérèse knew better.

What are these things in the eyes of God? Maybe a loveless thought carries worse implications. . . . And all could be resolved in His mercy.

Had she not told us how foolish it was to refer to the Almighty in terms of our own small-mindedness?

Her sense of proportion, even at the age of fourteen years, was infinite.

꙲

CHAPTER SIX

Campanula Pusilla, or The Little White Flower

I

THE TIME WAS drawing near when she felt she must tell her father of her desire to become a nun. It was her wish that she would find herself in Carmel by the following Christmas Eve, the date of the anniversary of her conversion.

She chose to speak to him on the evening of the Feast of Pentecost, and implored the Holy Spirit to make the occasion opportune.

Monsieur Martin, recovered from, but still a little enfeebled by, his recent illness, is sitting on a rustic bench on the lawn. His hair and beard are silver now. The last rays of the sun, a yolk of red fire behind the branches of the fir-trees, aureoles his slightly stooping head and shoulders as, hands clasped across the knob of his stick, he gazes into nowhere, with that air of vacancy which has descended upon him recently, perceptible only to the most astute, for outwardly it is not very different from his habitual attitude of contemplation.

It is very peaceful . . . just the muted birds, and the quiet resolving of the summer twilight . . . a lawn-mower stopping and starting a little way off, perhaps . . . distant garden voices. . . .

The slim, rather tall figure of a girl, in a white blouse and blue swinging skirt of pleated serge, appears in the doorway of the house, hesitates for a second, then treads lightly towards him, lit and unlit across the long shadows.

The old man—he is sixty-four now—suddenly aware of a presence, raises his head, smiles, and shifts up to make room for his daughter, his arm along the knobby back of the seat,

39

the hand, its skin shrunken and glossy, blotched with purple and brown, gently resting on her warm moving shoulders glimmering pinkly through the white stuff.

Thérèse rubs her cheek along his black lapel. Her hair is like filaments of pink gold.

"What is it, my little one?"

She cannot speak. Dew rises into her eyes. She swallows hard. And then it is out.

They walk up and down together.

Monsieur Martin weeps a little too, rather fondly and foolishly, as is the habit of the aged, but it is very affecting.

He says he had hoped she would stay with him till the end, but, God's will be done, he gives his consent.

Plucking a small white flower growing in the interstices of the garden-wall, he hands it to her as a symbol of her own life, which has been preserved so carefully until this day and will soon be transplanted into rarer soil.

The Little Flower . . . her popular name, in, as time goes, a comparatively few years, to be murmured by the lips of millions of suppliants all over the world. It is, admittedly, a sentimental-sounding epithet, but might that not be because the words "little" and "flower," charming in themselves, have deteriorated with the passing of time? Certainly, bad taste can be a form of hypocrisy, but is it not a worse hypocrisy to criticize excessively that which, dowdy as it may appear on the surface, is only the homely covering, the inadequate, yet heartfelt expression of something deeply loved? Would it be any more acceptable if she were to be referred to as *Campanula Pusilla?*—for that was probably the name of the herb Monsieur Martin gathered. But whether we like it or not—perhaps it is meant for a scandal to the sophisticated—the Little Flower is "the name wherewith she shall be called."

At last the tears are evaporated. The father and daughter are able to go in to supper with cheerful faces.

But it was not to be accomplished as easily as that.

The first obstacle to be placed in her path was the disapproval of her uncle and guardian, Monsieur Guérin.

France is the home of family conclaves. Even now important matters, such as what career to adopt, whom to marry, the best way to invest a legacy, etc., are often decided for younger members at a gathering of their elders, and we may be sure this custom was even more firmly adhered to in the nineteenth century.

Monsieur Guérin could not reconcile his avuncular prudence with the idea of a child of fifteen, as sensitive and highly-strung as his niece Thérèse, being permitted to embark on the rigorous life of a Carmelite nun. It would take a miracle, he admitted, to make him change his mind.

For three days the world went black for her. It rained as only it can rain in Lisieux. She had the delightful audacity to regard the weather, stormy or fine, as nature's expression of her own feelings!

Suddenly, miracle or no miracle, the sun came out again, and Monsieur Guérin revoked his decision.

Good. Now it was all right. Mother Marie Gonzague, the prioress, was waiting to receive her. They had only to make formal application to the Superior.

But here again she was in for a shock; and this time it was officialdom itself barring her way.

Canon Delatroëtte, narrow, correct, unbending, an icy damper of all enthusiasms, refused to consider the matter until she was twenty-one. It rained in torrents!

Shaken, but undaunted, she began to make arrangements to go with her father to appeal to the Bishop.

It was a morning at the end of October when they set off for Bayeux.

What was the weather?

Grey mist like moist wool, and the sun glimmering through, tiny as a red nail-head. Hopeful? . . .

She is dressed quite grown-up, has made herself a new costume for the occasion. Decent brown, with buttons down the side of the skirt. It can go to the poor later. She wears a little hat with wings, and—"wise as serpents, gentle as doves"—she has put up her hair so as to look older.

It is the first time she has paid a visit without one of her sisters. Pale and shining with nervous excitement, she shivers a little on her father's arm as they draw near the Bishop's house.

It begins to spit with rain, and she cannot forbear a few tears—or perhaps the order should be reversed? But she controls herself at the admonition of Father Révérony, the Vicar General, who receives them—"Ah, those diamonds! they must not be shown to His Lordship!" With outward composure she follows him, still on the arm of her father, through the tall ostentatious reception rooms which make her feel as insignificant as an ant.

Eventually they are issued into a parlor, warm and smelling faintly of incense. A bright animal-looking fire licks noisily behind a brass-knobbed fender. Three enormous heraldic-backed chairs, themselves as important-seeming as prelates, are ranged in a broken arc in front of it, the center one so massively ornate it looks like a throne.

Thérèse runs her kid fingers across the beads in her pocket, and glances at her father. Upright, militant, smiling reassuringly—but how old he looks today. His usually rosy cheeks have a yellowish mottled appearance. His every movement seems to require an abnormal amount of concentration.

Father Révérony returns, and makes way for the Bishop.

An entrance of brisk grandeur and benignity. She swoops down like a brown bird. A plump white hand with little black hairs on it, a circle of amethyst as big as a five-franc piece knocks her lips. The murmured blessing. She rises. Is he going to be kind?

Father Révérony motions her to the throne-like chair. But surely His Lordship ought to sit in that?

"Come," says the Vicar General. "Let us see if you know how to obey."

Immediately she deposits herself on the high bank of red plush. Her father sits in the chair at her side, the Bishop opposite. The too-big fire scorches her tense face, hiding, mercifully, her blushes.

There is an awful silence.

She had thought her father would explain the object of their visit, but, no, it is to be left to her. Very well, then. Bringing into power that magnanimity which is the other half of the positive antinomy whose base is humility, the whole secret of the force of sanctity, she begins, quietly, but unfalteringly, to insist on her vocation.

The ecclesiastics listen with a somewhat patronizing amusement. Her high seriousness does, perhaps, contain something comic. Then the Bishop suggests she is very young, surely it would be more sensible to stay with her father until she has reached the age of discretion—whenever that might be.

"But I have wanted to give myself to God since I was three!" she exclaims.

"It is quite true, your Lordship," supplements Monsieur Martin, adding respectfully, "and if the required permission cannot be obtained today, she will come with me to pray about it on a pilgrimage to Rome."

The Bishop is really surprised. It is the first time he has encountered a father as eager to relinquish his daughter as she is to offer herself.

"Well," he remarks, with that slow unctuous reasonableness always so irritating to zealots, whose desires leap unconstrainedly ahead of them, "we must first of all have a word with the Superior of Carmel, Canon Delatroëtte."

This is too much for Thérèse. She knows only too well what his answer will be. Despite her almost manly courage the ready tears well up, burning on her cheeks in the firelight like glittering opals. She keeps back all ugly sounds, crying silently, up-right in the big chair.

It would be enough to move a far more rigid man than the Bishop. He inclines forward, his pectoral cross dangling and flashing, and gently takes her hand.

"All is not lost, little one, but I am very glad you are going to Rome with your good father, it will strengthen your voca-tion, and, instead of weeping, you ought to rejoice. Next week I shall be at Lisieux and I will talk to the Superior about you. You shall certainly have my answer while you are in Italy."

2

They go into the garden to look at the last roses, but there are only charred buds, unopened, frost-bitten as her hopes.

His Lordship makes a little joke about her putting up her hair. Oh, it is all so utterly depressing, so exasperating! How much longer is she to endure these maddening delays? It is God's will, yes, it is His will, but she must do *something*. What now? To whom can she appeal next?

Suddenly it comes to her. The Pope!

※※

CHAPTER SEVEN

A Trip to Italy

I

THE DIOCESAN PILGRIMAGE seems to have been rather a snob-
bish affair. Its itinerary reads like a travel agent's pamphlet for
the grand tour. As well as Rome, the pilgrims were to take in
Paris, Milan, Venice, Padua, Bologna, Loretto, Naples, Pompeii,
Assisi, Florence, Pisa, and Genoa. Only the well-to-do could
have afforded it.

Toppers, spaniel-eared caps of tweed, tiered capes, chenille-
blobbed veils, plaid wraps, shooting-sticks and umbrellas of all
varieties, not to mention a diversity of gladstones, hat-boxes,
reticules, satchels strapped with easels, humped leather trunks,
and basket portmanteaus, were to descend from the chateaux
and grand villas of the department in a fussy overweening
stream, converging on the capital itself, from which bustling
center they were to embark in a specially labelled train.

It was rather a step-up for the Martins, who, although they
were comfortably off, were just that much lower in the social
scale than their companions as to be somewhat defensively
aware of it.

"It reminded us," remarked Thérèse herself, a trifle smugly,
"that we should not be 'solicitous for the shadow of a great
name.'"

She, and Céline, and their father, smartly but not osten-
tatiously clad beneath suitable shawl swathings, for it was
rather chilly, accompanied as far as the station by their aunt,
uncle, and cousins, had departed from Lisieux in an atmosphere of good wishes, anxious admonitions, and poignant wav-

ings of handkerchiefs, in the early morning hours when it was still excitingly dark.

Arriving in Paris, which did not impress her, she prayed her thanks again at the shrine of Our Lady of Victories, reaffirming the assurance that it really had been the mother of God who had brought about her cure.

She also prayed every day to St. Joseph, the father and protector of virgins, for she knew her passionate and impressionable nature might be lured to dally with sensible attractions, and she could not afford it.

It is said that a young man in the company fell in love with her, which might very well have happened, but there is little evidence to support it, and as she herself has made no comment we will not enlarge the rumor. She must have appeared undeniably attractive with her shining fairly-tale hair, her spontaneous exclamations, her whole being limned with the glow of her vocation.

The pilgrimage was consecrated to the Sacred Heart in the Basilica of Montmartre, glimmering high above the gas and naphtha-flares of the city's night-life, phosphorescent-white in the moonlight, as if it had been constructed from the bones of its martyrs.

At last the excited company, with all its paraphernalia, was safely packed in the box-like compartments, and the engine began to chuff in the direction of gay-hearted Italy!

Switzerland, through which they had to pass, was an unwinding panorama of loveliness. Vertiginous precipices, full of giant ferns and thread-like torrents, tumbled away beneath the rattling iron wheels. Lakes . . . peaks . . . hyacinth-blue snow . . . an Armageddon sunset . . . little peaceful villages with chalets clustered about a spire . . . a long black echoing tunnel, and out again into the fairy-world of dissolving, glittering enchantment!

Her brain became an album of these natural beauties, whose leaves would turn again in the voluntary prison of Carmel. The glory of God's creation made her mind reel. It was incredible to her that He had contrived all this for man to sojourn in for —how long had her illustrious mother, St. Teresa of Avila, said?—a brief "two hours."

Having contemplated the works of God, she turned to admire those of His creatures. Her ardor discountenanced taste. She went into an ecstasy over the dubious funeral statues in the Campo Santo at Milan, and had little patience with a somewhat fractious old gentleman who found the Martin enthusiasm rather tiring. But even he was entertaining. "How many different types of people we saw, and how interesting is the study of the world when one is about to leave it!"

Venice with its rippling palazzos, its terrible dungeons, the lugubrious Bridge of Sighs, and the harsh evocative cries of the gondoliers, stirring the misty airs over the lagoons like the calls of strange birds, she found contrastingly melancholy.

But everywhere there were relics to kiss, or to press one's rosary against. St. Antony's tongue in Padua, the body of St. Catherine in Bologna, the bowl of the Christ Child in the Holy House of Loretto, and in Rome itself the blood-soaked dust of the arena, the tomb of St. Cecilia in which Thérèse stretched herself as in a marriage-bed, the catacombs of St. Agnes, where, having begged a souvenir and been refused, a fragment of mosaic dropped from the ceiling into her hand, and—most wonderful of all—in the Church of Santa Croce, where she was able to push her little finger through the interstices of the jewelled coffer and actually touch two of the Thorns and one of the Sacred Nails.

"It is easy to see," she remarked, with a simplicity which disposed of any irreverence, "that I behaved towards Our Lord like a child who looks on its Father's treasures as its own, and thinks it may do with them as it pleases."

But we are rushing ahead of her. She is still in the train. It is night, and she has fallen asleep.

Suddenly her dreams are pierced by the cries of porters,

calling: "Roma! . . . Roma! . . ." across the jarring and shrieking of the slowing wheels.

Rome—the Holy City. They have arrived at last.

Owing to some hitch in the arrangements, there is no room
for them with the rest of the pilgrims at the Hotel di Milano,
and the Martins are directed to a less fashionable establishment,
the Hotel del Sud, in the Via Capo le Case. This small street,
probably not very salubrious even in those days, has deteriorated still further. The Hotel del Sud no longer exists. We
are told the building is now in use "for other purposes." There
are now two other hotels, a few private dwelling-places, several shops, and a brothel.

Can it be—is it possible?—that her presence now hovers
about these sordid little *chambres d'amour* in search of Mag-
dalens?

Admittedly, we have no real evidence that the house in
which she stayed has been so "converted," it is a speculation
merely, but why should it not be so? And, if so, why should
she not have gone back?

She said she would have been willing to be cast into hell if,
by so doing, she could have retrieved a single soul. It is very
feasible, then, that she, who was all love, should descend spiritually into an environment whose activities, however pervert-
edly, are nevertheless conducted under the auspices of that
abused yet sacred name. . . . Her infinite desire "to make love
loved" is probably, at this very moment, calling her into even
more unlikely places.

The Little Flower, despite her delicate title, was not easily
shocked. Something, we do not know what, caused her at this
time to be disappointed in the priesthood. She had been surprised to hear that the chief aim of the Carmelite Reform was
to pray for God's ministers whom she had "deemed purer than
crystals." She learned now that despite the high nobility of
their calling—and what could be higher?—they still remained
men and subject to human frailty. These lapses (whatever they

were) which she now witnessed only caused her to redouble the fervor of her intercession.

So . . . she had arrived in Rome, the focal point of her Faith. Or was that really Bethlehem?

Her main concern was to implore the Holy Father to grant her permission to enter Carmel at the age of fifteen.

The romantic beauty of ruins did not deceive her, although she loved the first day when they drove through the Campagna.

The center of the city, with its miscellaneous crowds, smart shops, and grand hotels, appeared no different from any other capital.

It is a strange place, Rome. She was not the only one to find it—unsatisfactory. There is a cleavage. The pagan city . . . the Holy City . . . but they have not fused. It is a woman who escaped from the arena, her side scarred by the lion. It is a battleground of angels and devils. The cleavage enters into the looker-on.

There was, is, of course, an exotic and seductive beauty. The exhalations of the antiquities, nostalgic tumbled temples, broken statues—breasts and knees pushed against drapes of stone—all the poignancy of the fallen grandiose, its tragedy dissolved by time and dust into the glittering ambience of a dream; and the art treasures, so numerous, so dazzling, as to make one's strained eyelids paralyzed with fatigue—it was good to rest high up in the Pincio Gardens in the afternoons, the shadows of whose leaves were like little faun's ears quivering in the golden-brown sunshine, or to drive slowly in a carozella through the cooling autumn night, the old cabman nodding over his bow of whip, in search of fountains. The enormous ones with figures, moon-white and mysterious, held her in a trance of water and stone, so that at times it was they, not she, who appeared to be moving. . . .

That terrible hub of lust, the Colosseum, from whose crumbling shell rang out the ghosts of shrieks and cheers, by day a time-pocked husk teeming with tourist ants, by night a snakepit of the vices, drew her inevitably. The original ground-level had been raised, but she and Céline would not be satisfied until they had clambered down a shaft, twenty-six feet deep, to touch the martyr's stone marked with a cross, and bruise their young mouths in the haunted sacred dust.

2

After a week of sightseeing, the momentous day arrived when the pilgrims were to be granted an audience with His Holiness Pope Leo XIII.

She awoke radiant with nerves and hope.

First they assisted at the Pope's Mass in his own private chapel at the Vatican. There was another mass of thanksgiving, and the audience began.

"Leo XIII, wearing a cassock and cape of white, was seated on a daïs, while round him were grouped various dignitaries of the Church. According to custom, each visitor kneeling in turn and kissing, first the foot (a custom since abandoned) and then the hand of the Sovereign Pontiff, finally receiving his blessing. At this moment, two of the Noble Guard placed their hands on the pilgrim's shoulder as a sign to rise and pass on to the adjoining hall. . . .

"No one uttered a word, but I was firmly determined to speak, when suddenly the Vicar General of Bayeux, Father Révérony, who was standing to the right of His Holiness, announced in a loud voice that *he absolutely forbade anyone to address the Holy Father.* On hearing this my heart beat wildly as if it would break, and I looked for counsel to Céline, who whispered: '*Speak!*'

"The next moment I was on my knees before the Pope. After I had kissed his hand, and then, raising my eyes, which were blinded with tears, I said imploringly: 'Holy Father, I have a great favor to ask of you.' At once he bent down towards me until his head almost touched my own, while his piercing

black eyes"—they were the eyes of a poet—"seemed to read
my very soul. 'Holy Father,' I repeated, 'in honor of your
jubilee, allow me to enter Carmel at the age of fifteen.'

"Surprised and displeased, the Vicar General said quickly:
'Holy Father, this is a child who desires to become a Carmelite,
and the superiors of the Carmel are looking into the matter.'
'Well, my child,' said His Holiness, 'do whatever the superiors
may decide.' Clasping my hands and resting them on his knee,
I made one last effort: 'Holy Father, if only you were to say
"Yes" everyone else would be willing.' He looked fixedly at
me, and said clearly, each syllable strongly emphasized: 'Well,
child! well, you will enter if it be God's Will!' Once again I
was going to plead, when two of the Noble Guard bade me
rise; seeing, however, that the request was of no avail, and that
my hands remained resting on the knees of His Holiness, they
took me by the arms, and with the help of Father Révérony,
lifted me to my feet. Just as I was being thus forced to move,
the dear Holy Father placed his hand gently on my lips, then,
raising it, blessed me, while his eyes followed me as I turned
away."

3

The ordeal was over, and she had failed.

The conflict of forcing herself to be disobedient to men in
order to be obedient to the Holy Ghost, the humiliation of
making a fool of herself in front of all these crowds of people,
the awful strain of having waited so long only to receive an
answer which, while it was not a definite refusal, could hardly
be termed positive—conform to her superiors, superiors who
seemed set unyieldingly against her!—resulted in a storm of
weeping, a further cause for misunderstanding. And, of course,
absurd, and exasperating, outside it was suddenly pouring with
rain! . . .

The rest of the trip was devitalized, her spirit seeping away through the pricks of disappointment in her heart, although she managed to control herself outwardly.

They went to Pompeii, where Vesuvius was obligingly dramatic, supplying a minor eruption. She walked in a group among the excavated streets, treading in the ruts of chariot-wheels, a waving pink ostrich plume of smoke above while beneath her feet the ground rumbled with an infernal indigestion. How much she would have preferred to be alone so as to ponder in peace "the instability of all things human."

The sumptuous hotels through which they passed, affording her glimpses of a world of luxury and sophistication, only served to increase her nostalgia to be "out of the swing of the sea," and safely hidden away in the enclosure.

Even a trip to Jerusalem, which her father offered her as a consolation, could be no substitute. She thanked him meekly and refused.

She likened herself to the infant Jesus's plaything, a mere ball which she referred to as being pierced by Him, and allowed to roll on one side while He slept. He was dreaming of her, perhaps, and one day He would wake up and clasp her to His heart.

Meanwhile she must continue to love Him in arid patience. No one must see how unhappy she was. The famous smile was considerably exercised.

They arrived home at the end of November, when she rushed to the hall-table in expectation of a reply from the Bishop. But there was nothing.

She turned her attention to being specially nice to poor Léonie, who had returned in silent ignominy from her over-rapturous attempt to become a Visitation nun.

Pauline, now Sister Agnes of Jesus, advised her from behind the grille to write again to remind His Excellency. Monsieur Guérin helped her to draft the letter, which was a model of French formality, containing an unconventional phrase for which he must have felt an unusual literary pride. It referred to Jesus. "I cannot resist the impulsion of the gentle violence He is putting upon me."

But the authorities seemed immune to her own gentle violence.

Christmas—that longed-for Christmas which she had hoped to celebrate in the radiant stillness of the cloister—came and went, and still there was no reply.

4

On New Year's Day, Mother Marie Gonzague wrote to tell her that "she had received the Bishop's answer authorizing her immediate entry into Carmel."

The letter shook in her hands. . . . It was too wonderful, she could hardly believe it!

She was right to doubt.

Such joy, it seemed, required some mitigation, for the making of a saint. The Prioress had decided to delay her admittance until after Lent.

❧

CHAPTER EIGHT

Fair World, Farewell

I

AND SO SHE waited in the winter world for the release of spring. . . .

The garden seemed a study in metallurgy. All the colors and textures were of metals: iron-black earth, the fir-trees as of green bronze, the fern-curls, which the new season would un-clench like tender baby fingers, were coiled now tight as clock-springs, and every twig and tendril oxidized by the frost.

But inside the doll's-house it was warm and comforting. Her father and sisters, solicitous for her well-being, and anxious to prove their affection for the "treasure" who was so soon to be taken from them, reduced the little rules of pious austerity, so that the window-panes reflected lights and fires against the snow, savory tit-bits were concocted in the kitchen, there was a general glow and odor of the delights of a happy home.

Like all of us, when we have screwed ourselves to a hard-won achievement and obtained it at last, the release of tension brought about a sudden relaxation in her. She let herself idle a little, or rather gave herself over to the natural relief of an organism which had been pressed to dislocation.

Now that at long last permission to enter had been granted to her, and it was no longer necessary to force her energies so single-mindedly in one direction, she became more aware of what she would be leaving behind. It was not only her beloved father and sisters, but the little things, her small household gods, that tugged at her heart. The way her spaniel, Tom, shoved his wet nose into her hands under the dining-table, her doves, their wings like music of Aeolian harps, sweeping down through the air for scattered grain, her old scarred satchel and school-books, the yellowing picture of her mamma in her wedding-dress, her butterfly-brooch, the pink sash, split and crumpled now, she had worn one Corpus Christi Day, and the little osier basket—she pulled it down, its gilt and ribbons dimmed and dusty, from a shelf in the wash-house—from which she had scattered rose-petals in the procession of the Blessed Sacrament. The odd memories attached to objects, often meretricious, broken, of no value in themselves, were poignantly disturbing.

This removal of restraint caused disconcerting fluctuations in her emotions, so that at times she would be filled with an airy happiness, causing the rooms to echo with bells of mischievous laughter, then the barometer of her spirits would unaccountably dip, and she would wander among her childhood possessions, her toys, and *bijouterie,* and pets, weeping sentimentally like a character in a romantic novel.

But this fanciful dishevelment did not last long.

Sitting before her dressing-table mirror one morning, dreaming, imagining herself in the habit of Carmel, pulling a long golden curl, and indulging in theatrically-tinted thoughts of the dramatic moment of sacrifice when it would be lopped, the absurdity, the danger of thus rhapsodizing came home to her with a jolt.

Vanity! Everything could be vanity if you let it—even becoming a nun. She made a simple act of contrition, and sobered-up. What did it matter?

As she was to say to her novices later on: "You should be glad when you fall . . . the very moment God sees us fully convinced of our nothingness, He reaches out His hand to us."

Everything a vanity? Everything could be a grace. The sweet, quiet, reasonable happiness flowed back into her, and she went down to help Léonie and Céline with the ordinary household tasks.

It was good to be so insignificant that you did not know what was going on in your soul. She took consolation from it.

Lent passed . . . Easter came, and the candles burning through the lilies on the altars were like the loving glances of her Lord. In a few days she will have nothing to do but to serve and live under that glowing benignity for the rest of her life. But it will not be quite as smooth as that. . . .

2

It is the evening of the 8th of April.

The red curtains are drawn close. A cheerful fire—no question of economy or austerity this day—is twinkling among the polished oak leaves and birds of the sideboard. The two painted glass lamps, carefully cleaned and trimmed by Léonie, have been brought from the mantelpiece to the round table. The best glass and silver, arranged for eight *couverts,* sparkles on the white linen, inset with motifs of Alençon, the handiwork of her departed mamma.

From the next room issues the aviary-chatter of excited voices, and the door opens to admit the family procession led by Monsieur Martin, with Thérèse, herself, all gold and white and hectic pink, under the protecting arm of her father. Next come Monsieur and Madame Guérin, her uncle and aunt, the former in scrupulously brushed black, his dangling pince-nez catching the fire-light, which also ripples along the looped curtain-like folds of his wife's new ink-blue bombazine. Their two daughters follow them. The elder, Jeanne, aged twenty, surprisingly smart in crackling cinnamon taffeta, is the only girl present who will not embrace the religious life—she is about to become engaged to a doctor, an up-and-coming Monsieur La Néele with an increasing practice in Caen. Her sister, Marie, a contemporary of Céline's—there is barely a year between them —will follow her cousins behind the grille when she is twenty-five. At present she is merely a pretty girl in her teens, delighting in a rather dowdy party-frock of geranium pink with a sash of lugubrious green, dyed and made-over from one of Jeanne's.

Céline in pale blue, and Léonie, already in her mid-twenties, resigned to a matronly black—she is not very interested in her appearance—make up the rear.

There is a scent of fire and eau-de-cologne, a sparkle of eyes and unostentatious jewelry. It is, of course, quite an occasion.

The pink glass center-piece on the table is stiff with real daffodils and artificial greenery, so the sweet breaths of flowers mingle with the savory smell of gravy.

Louise, broiled with kitchen heat and pride for her darling, her moustache glittering, her starched cap a little squiffy, enters, carrying high a huge steaming tureen.

Soon the wine is gurgling, knives and forks clicking, Madame Guérin's rings chime against the glasses, and the warm air is criss-crossed with bright conversation and laughter.

It is all very high-pitched, the gaiety precariously near to tears, but it is carried off successfully, individual feelings covered by conventional jokes and compliments in the true Gallic style.

The party lasts for about three hours, then the time comes for the guests to depart, farewells fading into the dark beyond the spill of light on the drive.

The Martins turn back into the house. The hilarity has subsided like the fire. Louise has blown out the lamps in the dining-room. Little intimate house-sounds remain, the ticking of the clocks, the cough of embers, a faint rattle of stirring claws on the perch under the green baize coverlet of the parrot's cage. Better to go to bed quickly. . . .

Undressed, in their room beneath the eaves, Céline and Thérèse turn and kiss each other good-night for the last time.

3

It is morning, very early.

Preparations for departure are made quickly and quietly. Everybody is tactful, smiling, controlling the emotions.

A second's passionate hug from Louise—Thérèse shakes under it—and they are out on the gravel waiting for Papa.

Here he is.

The little group, she and her father in the middle, move down the hill. The April sun shines on them like a watery eye. Workmen, shawled women, pause to watch. Occasional respectful acknowledgments.

Carmel draws nearer, by some strange hallucination of emotion seems to be moving towards them. . . .

The Guérins are already waiting at the gate.

The family enters. The church is full. There is a rustling, a turning.

Introit . . . Sacrifice . . . Holy Communion. The salver is passed from one member of the family to the other. Thanksgiving . . . *Ite Missa Est.*

Faint sobs, snuffles, in the incensed air. . . .

Thérèse rises, and leads the way to the cloister door.

It is a species of death.

Her bones are dissolving. She is nothing but a huge terrible-pounding heart. A vertiginous pause . . . a falling down, down, down into the depths of Abaddon . . . then, turning like a resurrection, her spirit rises. . . . Her loved ones are irradiated by the transcendent smile.

She knocks on the door. . . .

PART TWO

The Mountain of Carmel

꧁

CHAPTER ONE

Outside

I

IT WOULD SEEM a far cry from that "Carmel by the sea," that Elijah-haunted garden of delights of the Old Testament, whose declivities are odorous with the moisture of ferns, singing with gentle streams, and on whose brow, turned in the direction of the glittering blue Mediterranean, a gracious coronal of the cedars of Lebanon wave their stately arms like hailing prophetesses—a far cry, indeed, from that warmth to this coldness, the ugly red-brick Carmel of Lisieux, for that is how it strikes one on first acquaintance.

We cannot enter. It is an enclosure.

The church, however, is for everybody, and if we are very fortunate, for the nuns, of necessity, are sparing even of short interviews, we may be granted a few minutes in one of the parlors. Not that we shall see anyone—just a voice issuing through a black curtain, clear, crisp, pared of all superfluities, ringing pure as a clarinet, as we get up to depart, the reassuring watchword of the saint herself: *"Confiance! . . . Confiance!"*

Yet Carmel means a garden, and there is a garden, a quite lovely one, although hidden away behind the grim quadrangle, from whose gravel center protrudes a hideous tall concrete moulded cross, although we have only one or two difficult-to-come-by photographs to go on, and an odd descriptive word dropped here and there in her writings.

An orchard, and an *Allée des Maronniers.* . . . Although forbidden in actuality, later on we will walk there by the grace of our imaginations. She was able to visualize her beloved Abbé

Bellière only via a picture and her imagination, so she cannot mind.

The Carmel of Lisieux was founded in 1837 by two pious sisters, the Mlles. Goiselin, who wished to use their small fortune for that purpose. Apart from their life of contemplative prayer, their true *raison d'être,* the nuns supported themselves by the manufacture of altar-breads, incense, and church ornaments. At this period the holy poverty, to which they were devoted, did not require much cultivation—they were often so poor that they could not supply habits for intending postulants.

The Order of Discalced (*i.e.* barefooted) Carmelite Nuns was founded in 1562 by St. Teresa of Avila, and it is her vigorous, yet delicate-minded, personality, which has become imbued in, is, one might say, the spirit of Carmel. Despite their austerities, her nuns were encouraged to be gay. A bout with a tambourine, for example, was considered a good cure for lowness.

The communities, usually limited to under twenty nuns (the Lisieux Carmel, by a special concession, is allowed to be slightly larger), are, within the form of the rule, permitted to develop individually.

Usually, there, the day begins at about five o'clock, and concludes about eleven-thirty. Between compline, which ends at about nine, and the following Matins, the Great Silence prevails, as it does in most religious houses.

Carmelite nuns wear a rough frieze habit, consisting of a brown under-dress and scapular, a white cloak fastened at the throat with a wooden peg, simple white headbands, and a black veil. Their feet are bare but for the primitive Spanish *alpargates* or hempen sandals.

They abstain perpetually from meat, and eat only one main meal a day from September 1st until Easter. As well as the recital of the Divine Office, two hours daily are spent in mental prayer.

Harsh as these regulations may sound, an atmosphere of extreme lightness and sweetness prevails—at least, that is the ideal. It is a world of spiritual athleticism, albeit essentially gentle and feminine. Who knows—the energy generated by these quiet-humming hidden dynamos, or to put it more graciously, these beehives of perpetually murmured prayer, is saving mankind from a worse fate than has already befallen it . . . ?

Since the canonization of Sister Thérèse in May 1925, and the ensuing influx of pilgrims, it has been found necessary to enlarge the chapel and precincts, but the same nineteenth-century background of consecrated grimness remains.

The actual edifice is tasteless and unbeautiful, yet there is a kind of smiling sweetness playing over the narrow cramped altars and innumerable plaques of thanks for the saint's intercession which it would be ungrateful to deny. The interior is veneered from head to foot with these *ex-votos,* or formal stone visiting-cards of the devout.

Above the High Altar, behind a semicircular arch, there is a sculptured representation in plasticine-grey of the saint receiving roses from the kirtle of the Blessed Virgin and scattering them over the globe. "When I die I will let fall a shower of roses," she prophesied. This is not it. But it serves.

To the right the huge grille of iron bars, like a medieval portcullis, from behind which the invisible nuns assist at the Mass, seems to open on to depths of blackness like the "dark night." At one side there is another smaller grille, like a *guichet,* where they may receive Holy Communion. As a sign that one of them is kneeling there, a finger may be seen to emerge to switch on the tiny electric bulb at the side of a little red window-curtain.

The design for the actual tomb of St. Thérèse, its heavily embossed coffer in any case much too big for the small side chapel containing it, has apparently been derived from some bourgeois conception of either the Sleeping Beauty or Snow White—it would be difficult to decide which; probably the latter, for her effigy reclines in a coffin of glass.

The figure, slightly under life-size—a morbid conception

common to the makers of wax-works—reposes on plump cushions, the pretty face, crowned with a wreath of paper roses, inclined with an expression of suitable, or, rather, unsuitable, saccharinity towards the spectator. She is already turning yellow like those wax dummies in old-fashioned ladies' outfitters. They have dressed her in an apotheosis of the habit of Carmel —rather rubbed-looking brown velvet, sewn with seed pearls. In her clasped hands she carries the Golden Rose presented to her by the Pope.

The marble floor below the daïs, inset with a pink tesselation of that flower, is heaped with the petals of real roess. Their fragrance steals about the ugliness, breaths of pure devotion in a tawdry world. . . .

The *Salle des Reliques,* a large room opening off the sacristy, is something of an ordeal for those whose sense of fitness outweighs their devotion.

We take our places in a queue to file past what appears to be the crowded window of a departmental store.

A large full-length oil-painting of the saint occupies the center-back. She is walking in the garden, crossed by a theatrical sunbeam. There are other pictures, by Pauline, depicting scenes from her sister's life. They, at least, are unpretentious.

Either side the commissioned portrait, two heavily carved mahogany screens, reminiscent of Victorian wardrobes, display her habits as novice and nun. We had always understood her clothes were patched to the last thread. These garments look new, or certainly as unspotted as if they had just been returned from the cleaners. Perhaps one of them is the fresh habit she was given in the year of her death.

It was apparently very ill-fitting and uncomfortable. When asked if it inconvenienced her, such was her detachment, her complacency almost, she replied: "Not a jot! No more than if it was that of a Chinese, away there, two thousand leagues from us."

There is her first Communion dress, and another frock she

wore for a Corpus Christi procession, her little table, cutlery and drinking-bowl, a pair of sandals (perhaps these merely represent the kind she wore, for it has been mentioned that her own were so completely worn-out that, after her death, they were thrown on the fire by a lay-sister zealous for tidiness, who was not going to have that rubbish cluttering up the convent), her palette and paint-brushes, examples of the artificial flowers with which she decorated the Altar of the Christ Child, and her instruments of penance, including a knotted cord discipline, two horse-hair belts, a wire-mesh bracelet for the upper arm, and the barbed cross which she very sensibly discarded when it made a sore on her breast. We shall have more to say on this subject later. They are set out in a glass case, pinned into position there by coral and topaz brooches, offerings of the devout. To see these objects, which were meant to cause pain, thus decorated gives a peculiarly disturbing effect.

But the *pièce de résistance* of the collection is her hair. It hangs in the carefully arranged undulations of the *perruquier,* like the wig of the sleeping beauty in a pantomime. There is so much of it doubters might imagine it to have been added to. It has no sheen, the paper lilies crowning it are faded and dusty, and it has been reassembled in such a way as to give the impression that instead of being shorn at her Clothing, she was scalped!

The vulgarity of the presentation of these *objets* is an obscuration, and one wonders just how much longer it will be before, to use an appropriate expression, she will blow the lid off the coffee-pot! At the same time it must be remembered that by these tasteless concessions she has been able to draw to the good life countless millions who would otherwise, probably, have languished in a clutter of bric-à-brac, both mental and physical. Since the advent of St. Thérèse antimacassars and aspidistras have taken on a different complexion. Woe betide any of us now who dare to sneer at what we consider an affront to our æsthetic sensibilities. One just cannot be sure . . . and, in any case, æstheticism is not the point.

But for the favored there is a special treat waiting, and this, indeed, does for a few moments bring one into the presence of reality. Roget, the sacristan, fussy, egregious with the consciousness of his important office, a true humility probably, opens a little door and beckons us after him to see, first, the authentic wooden "turn" on which—when she served in a like capacity to himself—she reverently placed the articles of the Mass, to swivel them round to the priest in the church at the other side of the wall (she liked to see her reflection inside the chalice, shining a welcome for her Lord . . .); and, secondly, the original flagstones and door to the enclosure—it was here that she knelt to receive her father's blessing before bidding *adieu* to the world.

We may push the turn as she did, like her kneel on these very stones—kiss them if we are so inclined. . . .

Because it is simple, a little hidden away, not, as it were, floodlit in the Church's shop-window, there is a real pleasure in this, a thrill of delight which is by no means a paralyzed awe. This is the actual "turn" she pushed. Her delicate fingers, the knuckles probably chipped and red with chilblains (the endurance of cold was an extremity of penance to her—"I nearly died of it," she said), must have really touched these segments of shelf. . . . Smiling at ourselves, for it is absurd and childlike, we insert our own hand and gently trundle the contraption round. . . .

So this, then, is the place. At the risk of heresy, one might say, this is the mecca. This is how it looks from the outside. But outsides can be very deceptive. . . .

2

It is the eve of her feast.

The rain has ceased, but scarves of moisture still float in

the rheumy autumn air. The potholes are full of black water. How dark it is! An occasional lamp flickering on a corner . . . the mask lights of the cabins and the few remaining tall houses. . . . A flood of yellow spills out of the chapel as the doors are pushed back to make way for the procession.

Her bones, what is left of them (her body was not intact at the exhumation—she had said it would not be), are brought out, appropriately, by youths. They lurch the gold *chasse,* surprisingly simple and beautiful, on to their not very stalwart shoulders, and set off. She is to be carried round the town, resting for the night in the Cathedral of St. Pierre.

A car with a loudspeaker noses its way in a company of Oblates of St. Thérèse, an order of unenclosed nuns who busy themselves with the more external works of charity, such as sweeping the rooms of the aged, hoeing potatoes, nursing the sick. Their white veils, luminous in the darkness, give an air of sameness, but their faces are all different, though mainly young.

The faithful follow in an uneven throng, straggling in and out of the puddles, their devotional candles shoved through paper cartons depicting Our Lady of Lourdes. Holy poverty again, it seems. She has had to borrow from another cultus. The little flames, dim and brownish in their auras of mist, illuminate protecting hands, the underparts of chins, noses, and eye-sockets.

The car contains priests who take it in turns at the microphone. Their histrionic, emotional-sounding prayers are amplified into the night:

> *"Sainte Thérèse, intercédez pour nous!*
> *Sainte Thérèse, ayez pitié de nous!*
> *Sainte Thérèse! . . . notre petite Thérèse, daignez*
>   *nous bénir!*
> *Sainte Thérèse, revenez à Lisieux! . . . revenez*
>   *dans notre monde qui souffre! . . ."*

The flickering, stumbling procession winds on through the narrow broken ways. The sceptical, or weary, gaze down in muted curiosity. It is nothing new to them. They have seen it all before. One must live. Children come, but not bread. The granaries are piled with bombs. What is the use of prayers?

"Sainte Thérèse, ayez pitié de nous! . . ."

We pass gaps, heaps of shards, new scaffolding.

Behind us, a cross of white electric bulbs shines out from the roof of Carmel.

Sordidness, depression, hope, faint and stooping like the candles. Some have gone out.

Ahead, the gold casket seems tossed on crying human waves.

"L'air de la terre me manque," she said, when she was dying. It is so.

"Sainte Thérèse, hâtez vous de nous exaucer!
Sainte Thérèse, revenez dans ce monde qui se meurt. . . ."

🏵

CHAPTER TWO

Inside

I

THERE IS A curious paradox about the nineteenth-century Carmel of Lisieux, a paradox, to a greater or lesser extent, common to most religious communities. We are referring to the sweet-and-bitter, almost startling mixture compounded of playfulness, homeliness, small childlike pleasures, ugliness, hardship, and deliberate, one might even say cruel, mortification.

By concentrating on one aspect to the neglect of the other we should receive a biased and totally inaccurate impression. Yet it is very difficult to steer a middle course, for the joys often hide sorrows, and *vice versa*. We may be smiling patronizingly at what seems like an indulgence in sentimentality, to find, suddenly, that what a moment ago appeared to be a sugarplum has turned into a cold hard stone.

Fortunately the metamorphosis also works the other way round, and instead of a sharp-sided flint we discover we are holding a rose. It is all very strange, very mysterious . . . we would do well to think carefully before arriving at any definite conclusion, and even then, so evanescent is our comprehension of things spiritual, the whole truth may, probably will, have eluded us. Indeed, we shall never get at the key by mere empiricism. The touchstone is faith.

Thus it would be possible to think of Thérèse's new abode as a slightly hilarious happy family, made up of feminine titters over feast-day charades, not very exacting devotions conducted among borders of flowers, the interchange of little gossipy notes delivered from cell to cell by fairy postmen, and mitigations of the Rule to eat woodcock, expensive lobster, or suck at toffee-apples.

On the other hand, one could see it as a parade of close-lipped repression, the haggard Brides of Christ clasped by horse-hair belts and cutting chains, arranging flagellations with bunches of nettles, fasting to the point of exhaustion, all this to the accompaniment of howling winds blowing through the exposed cloisters—a species of death-in-life bordering on the insane.

Certainly the younger novices were encouraged to whip tops, but they were also encouraged to whip themselves; one would have to be very particular before deciding which they did most.

In actuality it was probably neither so amusing nor so sensational, merely humdrum. But the charming, and the terrifying, elements were undoubtedly there. The economy of such a life is expensive. One cannot embark on it without touching extremes.

But there will be no need to search for the dramatic. It will come quite naturally from the play of souls.

As with all human institutions, the ton oef a Carmel is set by its superiors.

In 1888, at the time of Thérèse's reception, the Carmel of Lisieux was motivated by two influences, the slightly lax gentleness of Mother Geneviève, the original Prioress, and the somewhat harsh vigor of her successor, Mother Marie Gonzague. It is perhaps necessary to exaggerate a little in order to make the contrast clearer, though neither of these two women was entirely dominated by her chief characteristics.

Mother Geneviève's influence was on the wane. Her forbearance and sweetness now radiated from the infirmary. In three years she will be dead. But Mother Marie Gonzague was all over the place, and very much alive. You never knew where her zealous admonitions were likely to pop up. She was still a comparatively young woman, under fifty, physically very strong, but splenetic, which made her unpredictable. She was subject to moods, changed her mind, suddenly descended on some little thing, a personal failing or a slight task left undone, and gave vent in a way which, for those who did not understand her, was undoubtedly rather alarming.

As we shall see, she was strict to the point of unkindness with Thérèse. She had a good reason for this, though she was probably not always ruled by it. It would be easy, indeed tempting, to make Mother Gonzague into the villainess of the piece. It would also be grossly unfair. It seems that, fundamentally, she had a better understanding of her new charge than the kind, sympathetic Mother Geneviève.

The latter was credited with a sort of spiritual clairvoyance, but it did not tell her much about Thérèse. Except once, in a dream, when a deceased member of the community, a Sister Adelaide, returned carrying an ivory penholder with which she pointed out on a shelf, next to the New Testament, another book, on the spine of which was written with an irritating secrecy: "Life of . . .".

It was, apparently, a prophecy, denoting the importance which would one day be attached to "The Story of A Soul," St. Thérèse's autobiography. But neither Mother Geneviève nor the abbé she sent for to consult with on the matter could understand what Sister Adelaide was getting at, which was not very surprising. The old lady had certainly remarked the novice's aspirations, had indeed been a little intimidated by them, but Thérèse had, as yet, offered no evidence to suggest that she would one day become a best-seller!

Before pursuing the story it might be as well to glance at the new protagonists. At least fourteen of the twenty-odd nuns are identifiable.

Sister Agnes of Jesus (Pauline) had been permitted to take up the new hobby of photography, so we will let her make a composite group of those whose lives impinged upon that of Thérèse. She can set the shutter, and sit in the picture herself.

For our purposes we may be permitted to play a trick with

time and let them all pose together, though in actual fact it would have been impossible to assemble each and every one in the same instant, for some would have died and some would not yet have arrived.

Although at the time of writing one, at least, is still alive, we must imagine ourselves to be looking at a conclave of ghosts. Alive or dead, in the eight-year orbit of Thérèse's stay in Carmel their impact remains.

Mother Geneviève and the Prioress, Mother Marie Gonzague, we have already introduced, and it will not be necessary to describe again Thérèse's three natural sisters, Sister Agnes of Jesus (Pauline), Sister Marie of the Sacred Heart (Marie), Sister Geneviève of the Holy Face (Céline), not due to arrive until 1894; Marie Guérin will come in 1895 and will be known as Sister Marie of the Eucharist. Here is Sister Marie of the Angels who was Sub-Prioress and Novice Mistress when Thérèse arrived. Her features are somewhat loosely articulated, a sign of garrulity. She was kind and wished to be helpful, but Thérèse was unable to confide in her and found her winning ways rather a trial. Sister Marie of St. Joseph is neurotic, poor thing. She is fully professed, but is shut away behind incommunicable barriers—a terrible double immolation. Her job is the sorting and mending of the linen, a task which is the means of a slight but deeply sympathetic contact between herself and the saint. Sister Marthe of Jesus, passionate and over-emotional, will conceive a too sensible attraction to the Prioress, and Thérèse will help her to sublimate it or, more appropriately, give it its fullest expression. Here is Sister Saint Pierre, old and exacting, mumbling in a fume of exasperation over her stick because she is not well-placed in the photograph. Sister Marie of the Trinity, one of Thérèse's novices, will be assisted by her to full profession over a novitiate strewn with obstacles. Beautiful Sister Madeleine, after being nursed devotedly by the saint, will die in the influenza epidemic of 1891. Then there is

the little nun who rattled her rosary to Thérèse's nervous irritation until she decided to listen to it as if it were music, and
the other one, also nameless, for whom the saint had such an
antipathy that she would have gone out of her way to avoid
her, had she not decided to cultivate an affection for her which
was so noticeable as to be almost misunderstood. And there
are at least another half-dozen, one or two of whom we shall
probably have occasion to mention, but whose lineaments we
will leave blank to be filled in by the speculations of the reader,
for one of the chief objects of this work is to touch off innumerable imaginations.

They are not literary creations we are dealing with but real
people, so we can never be sure of them. The mutations are
endless.

A hive of whitewashed corridors with little cells containing
a truckle bed, a table and chair, and the appliances for the
simplest toilet, the choir, the refectory, the common-room for
recreation with its few bookshelves and battered halma-board—
the knobs of the green and scarlet pieces are quite greasy-black
—the infirmary (now turned into a chapel), the kitchen with
its oven and cabbage smell, the draughty cloisters and gravel
quadrangle, and the gardens and outhouses, in one of which
stands the machine for stamping out the Hosts, falling like
confetti or snowflakes into the linen-lined basket placed beneath,
and another in which old Sister Anne (shall we call her?)
pounds her pestle, and instructs one novice in her secret recipes,
the heady perfumes of her gums and essences drifting across
the yard to outwit the inadequate drains.

Such is the inside, but we must try to go inside the inside.

Everyone is busy in Carmel. It is as active really as an adventure story.

But let us permit ourselves one romantic digression in the
Chestnut Walk, and then we will resume our task and begin
to climb the mountain.

2

It is an evening in early summer, and the time of the Great Silence.

Compline is over. The thin sweet wail has died away among the shadows of the rafters, and the community has separated to its individual commitments until the morning.

She sits outdoors in a little cave-like structure, half-arbor, half-grotto—Hermitage St. Madeleine it says inscribed in poker-work over the doorway—a nook such as her mother, the great-hearted St. Teresa of Avila, liked to rest in between her jogging journeys over the rock-strewn roads of Spain. But her little daughter will stay put.

The sky between the interstices of the candelabra-like branches is gradually changing from pale dying silver to the butterfly-blue of night. The stars, faintly distinguishable . . . a last bird twittering down to sleep with that queer little noise like a wet cork rubbed on a tumbler . . . the frogs near the stream at the bottom of the meadow are beginning to stutter "Er-er . . . er-er-er. . . ." Another nun, so withdrawn and bowed into her habit as to appear anonymous, passes and repasses the mouth of the hermitage at intervals, silently reciting her rosary to the garden air before retiring. It is an hour such as she has shared—how long ago?—with her beloved Céline in the attics of Les Buissonnets. But now she communes with her Maker alone.

"He shall cover thee with His wings," they have been singing, "and under His feathers shalt thou trust." That androgynous omniscient God who is both a father and a mother . . . who is everything.

As her earthly father would have said, using the bucolic idiom of Normandy, she has been "drawn out from under the cart" at last.

The nuns have been very kind—tonic wine and fur slippers have been provided, concession to her youth and delicate constitution, and Monsieur Martin, *le facteur de Jésus*, is forever at the turn thrusting in veritable cornucopias of vegetables and parcels of fish.

God has begun by tempering the wind. But the petting will not last. She will see to that herself. And already Mother Marie Gonzague has started her fault-finding. Yesterday when she had been instructed to go and weed the border, the Prioress, recreating with a little company of sisters, had uttered, *en passant,* but in tones which were obviously meant to be overheard: "What sort of a postulant is this, who has to be sent out for a walk every day!" And this morning the bewildered child, unused to performing the chores of a servant, had been called to order in front of the whole community because she had omitted to bring down a cobweb when sweeping the cloister.

And that is not all. She is summoned again and again to the Reverend Mother's room to be chided for her laziness and incompetence. She admits she is very slow—her practical responses seem numbed. What can she do? She resolves to spend the greater part of her free time continuing sewing, her needle plucking in the darkness because another nun has mistakenly gone off with her—our, she should say—lamp.

It does not matter. For she enjoys a peace which is independent of what happens to her. These apparent slights are mere taps on the alabaster, that vase of sweet-smelling unguents which is herself, and which must, at last, be broken to delight her Lord.

At first there had been a sensible pleasure in having achieved her object, in having arrived in the desert which was, by the divine praising, to blossom like the rose, although Canon Delatroëtte's devastating utterance on her admittance—"I present to you the child you have coveted. I hope she will not

disappoint your expectations, but should it so fall out, I remind you that the responsibility is your own"—still rang like
a knell in her soul.

It was so lovely to be near Pauline and Marie again. But
such obvious natural joys were already beginning to fade. She
and Pauline, whom we must always think of now as Sister
Agnes of Jesus, had, in the course of the rota, come together
over setting the table in the refectory, but it had seemed to
Thérèse that her sister, her little mother, as she liked to regard
her, no longer knew her. It was not strange. She knew why it
appeared so. But it gave her a pang.

And she was suddenly spiritually dry, was, indeed, to remain
in that condition for the rest of her earthly sojourn.

What is spiritual dryness? What does it mean?

It has been called, most irritatingly, a sign of grace. This
definition can only be explained by the transcendent aspira-
tion of the soul—a grace indeed—beating its wings against the
mortal prison house. The door can be, will be, unlocked from
the other side. But the soul of itself can do nothing. The very
awareness of its captivity is then a grace. Inevitably such height-
ened and temporarily thwarted consciousness is often extremely
painful. It can only be made meaningful, and thus endurable,
by, in the worst cases, the extremities of patience, and a quiet
or wrung-forth gratitude that it should be allowed to know the
infinitude of its desires. It is a lack of response on the plane
on which feeling is customary which makes it so depressing,
but it should be remembered that it is often the prelude, however long drawn out, to an ecstasy which could not be experienced without this sensible dying.

St. John of the Cross, loved friend of St. Teresa of Avila,
and favorite devotional writer of our Thérèse, knew everything
about it. But this is neither the time nor the place to become
involved in the convolutions of mysticism. She herself found
no necessity to do so; and although, since, her intellect has

been placed on a level with that of St. Thomas Aquinas, admitted her inability.

She was feeling very low, and any kind of rational understanding of her aridity was for the time being in abeyance—incidentally one of its most distressing concomitants.

Temporary comfort did arrive in the form of a Jesuit priest, Father Pichon, who told her, after she had made a general confession, that he was convinced her soul was in a state of baptismal innocence, and that she had never committed a mortal sin.

This is hardly surprising. There is no mortal sin except by a deliberate cutting oneself off from the divine mercies, and when was she likely to have done that? But his words were a thrilling consolation.

Almost immediately he was sent on a mission to Canada.

He had lightened her heart, but the state of aridity remained.

Why, then, veiled by these sadnesses, sitting in the garden whose very dews were suggestive of tears, did the smile continue to break? It seems such a pathetic, morbid, one might almost say silly, contradiction.

Was her expression of happiness contrived and artificial, a simulated idiotic gaiety merely, the outcome of a perversely inverted egotism, which in the world might have expressed itself by a flaunting of her beauty, a domination of lovers, a triumphant power and acquisitiveness? Was she performing an intricate and dangerous balancing act on the tight-rope of a strained-to-breaking will?

Some, in their quite laudable desire to dispose of the softness and sentimentality with which the timorous, the devout equivocators, have draped their darling, have thought it to be so. True, she was not compounded of sugar and rosewater. True, she was as cutting and resilient and flashing as tempered steel. But to reply as she replied to the nuns who questioned and misunderstood her when she was dying, "It was not that."

What was it, then? The answer is really so simple. It was—
but wait. It will reveal itself, in the course of the story.

The moon is rising . . . the elevation of a dazzling Host.
She gets up and moves quietly in the direction of her cell.

❦

CHAPTER THREE

The Postulant

I

1888 . . . Paris is ringing with hammers.

Next year is to herald the opening of the World Fair.

A weird tower is going up the like of which has never been seen before, built entirely of iron, a thousand feet high, its metal legs straddling the houses on the left bank like, as one of the new symbolist poets might have said, an image of death. And indeed it does have the appearance of a huge skeleton, its top ghastly pin-headed like a skull, falling back against the sky when you look up at it. It is to be the means of many suicides. A Monsieur Eiffel has designed it, and the success of its strong tense girders is to suggest later, to another man, the construction of the airplane.

Not very far away, but hidden, being rapidly accreted—but not so rapidly—in silence, is another tower, one whose life will offer the means of carrying souls into life, not death, and when, like the other, it is to spread wings, will drop, instead of bombs, a freight of roses, innumerable blessings.

The soon-to-be-rising tower of Thérèse is first firmly establishing its foundations.

Her letters at this time betray little of her inward feelings. They are the epitome of the Carmel tradition of gaiety. The old nicknames persist. In writing to her father she is still the "Orphan of the Berezina," and at the opposite extreme the "Queen of France and Navarre." Sister Agnes is the "fine pearl," and Sister Marie the "diamond" and the "gipsy."

It is almost as if she were deliberately hiding her intensity under a guise of frivolous petted childishness. Everyone is so kind, she must always be warming her feet and sipping the tonic wine, she has never eaten so much in her life! She does not find it necessary to mention that the increased diet is heavy and gives her indigestion, nor that she is in the habit of sprinkling wormwood on her food to make it less palatable.

This, like the wearing of the pointed cross, was a mortification she was soon to renounce, but however mistaken—and she was quick to realize that it was so—it was the way she started. Like the little mermaid in Hans Andersen, she danced on knives. . . . The smile, for the time being, had become the least bit tautened.

It may well be asked what is the point of mortification? And indeed to the misinformed it may appear as a superstitious morbidity, or an inverted form of indulgence in the sensuality the practitioner has, on the surface, given up. But Thérèse quickly learned about those species of self-deception, as we shall see.

The highest form of love is undoubtedly sacrifice. Sacrifice, being the relinquishment of self, involves a kind of pain. This may be brought about in two ways, by a glad acceptance of one's lot, or by a deliberate seeking of what is disagreeable to the natural man in order to make a voluntary gesture of unselfishness.

The latter method is common to ascetic temperaments. It is is fruitful in that it strengthens, and enables the individual to know himself better, though these by-products are not the main point. True mortification rises from a love of God, a kind of exasperation of the soul seeking continually to do something more for its Beloved.

And as loving is a kind of folly it is, of course, possible to fall into excesses. Therein lies the difference between mortification and morbidity. But one should be slow to challenge. What might be extravagance in one might be the fullest expression in another, and *vice versa*.

There have been, are, perhaps, men and women who have

entered into seemingly frightful conditions of self-abasement, whilst at the same time retaining and increasing the most virile healthy-mindedness.

St. Bernard kept his eyes so lowered that he did not know how many windows were in the church; St. Dominic scourged himself with iron chains until the wall of his cell was splashed with blood; Blessed Benvenuta Bojani wore an iron girdle that eventually embedded itself into her flesh; Blessed Columba slept on a bare table; Blessed Henry Suso reclined on a door studded with nails, he also incised the initials of the Holy Name over his heart and refrained from drink until his tongue split with thirst; Père Lacordaire does indeed seem to have arrived dangerously near the border-line—amongst the most wretched macerations he also encouraged his fellows to buffet him, spit in his face, and address him by abusive names. Yet none of these people were mad—the general tenor of their lives proves them to have been remarkably sane.

However, such violent methods are fortunately not for everybody. St. Francis of Assisi made a bonfire of his monks' hairshirts. And St. Thérèse, figuratively speaking, did the same.

While continuing to adhere to the conventional penances of the Rule, the silence and fasting, the taking of the discipline— she refused to resist the self-inflicted blows by any stiffening of the body—she at the same time sought out another way, a way in complete conformity with her own personality. She had come to Carmel to suffer, and suffer she would, but it would be unobvious.

As time went on she did not find it necessary to seek penances. She merely accepted every small inconvenience gratefully.

At the same time she was still prudent. When told of a holy priest who chose to endure an irritating skin disease without once making a movement to relieve it, she remarked: "Yes . . . but I should not have been able to forbear and preoccupy my mind thus. God does not, as we imagine, confine Himself to the consideration of a host of small things, and in nothing must we oppress our soul." Yet we should be careful not to confuse the little instance with its enormous effect.

It has been rightly said that some souls are strong enough for big things but not strong enough for little things. Think how difficult it could be to glide gracefully through bone-piercing winters without even chafing one's fingers, to sweat over the rubbing-boards of the stuffy laundry and endure the splashing of dirty water without making the slightest attempt to mop one's brow, to apply one's interested attention to the chatter of boring colleagues at recreation as if commonplaces were exactly the words one wished most to hear . . . of such unnoticeable but excruciatingly painful examples was her particular way of mortification compounded.

Often and often she longed to call in at the Mother Superior's cell for a word of consolation, but she never did so. She sat on the stairs, her whole being shaking, then dragged herself up by the banister to her apportioned place of silence and loneliness where it seemed, for the time being, even her beloved Lord refused to enter.

But this apparently meaningless conglomeration of minutiæ, because enkindled by charity, was one day to burst out in beacon fires that would flame across the world.

"In order that Love may be wholly satisfied," she said, "it must stoop even to nothingness and transform that nothingness into fire."

Thérèse, in her desire to become as infinitesimal as a grain of sand, no, as an atom, was to generate such a force of energy that its effects would reverberate into Eternity!

Meanwhile there was nothing noticeable about her but her charm.

The gardener used to watch for her coming, and pause in his work to remark her passing. Although she did not so much as deviate her head from its forward glance under the veil, he always knew when it was she.

Her gift for mimicry—she was not so solemn as to repress

her mischievousness, which would remain with her to her death-bed—caused her to be very popular at recreation.

"Oh dear, there won't be any laughs today," the nuns would exclaim, if for some reason she was prevented from attending.

That was all . . . just a charming girl, vague to the point of stupidity sometimes, but so sweet really, and very amusing. A saint? Such a fantastic idea had not entered anyone's head.

And even when she was dying, and those of the community who had been privileged to enter into some intimacy with her knew what they were in the presence of, she was still able to overhear a lay-sister commenting to another: "I wonder what Reverend Mother will find to say in Sister Thérèse's Obituary Notice? She's never really done anything. . . ."

It was quite true, in a way. "God will not judge me according to my works," she said, "for I haven't any. He will judge me *according to His own.*"

On the surface it seemed to be merely a question of whittling oneself down. Irritating, to some extent. One would not like to count the number of times she had recourse to the expression "little" and its synonyms, but the balance was perfect, for on the opposite point on the circumference her magnanimity knew no bounds.

"To be Thy spouse, O Jesus, to be a Carmelite, to be by my union with Thee the Mother of Souls—all this ought to suffice me. Yet I feel within me other vocations; I feel the vocation of warrior, priest, of apostle, of doctor, of martyr. . . . I would accomplish all the most heroic works, I feel the courage of a crusader, I would die on the field of battle in defence of the Church. A priest's vocation! With what love, O Jesus, would I hold Thee in my hands when my voice had caused Thee to come down from Heaven! With what love would I give Thee to souls! But, alas, even when desiring to be a priest, I admire and envy the humility of St. Francis of Assisi, and I feel the vocation to imitate him by refusing the sublime dignity of the priesthood. How unite these contrasts? I would enlighten souls, as did the prophets and doctors. I would travel over the earth to preach Thy name and plant Thy glorious cross on heathen soil, O my beloved; but one mission alone would not satisfy me; I would at the same time proclaim the gospel in every part of the world, even in the most distant isles. I would be a missionary, not only for a few years, but I desire to have been one since the creation of the world, and to continue to be one even to the consummation of the ages. O, but above all I desire martyrdom. Martyrdom—this was the dream of my childhood, a dream that has grown with me in my little cell of Carmel. But this is another folly, for I desire not only one kind of torture; in order to satisfy myself I must have them all. . . .

"Like Thee, my beloved Spouse, I would be scourged, crucified. . . . I would die flayed like St. Bartholomew; like St. John I would be plunged in boiling oil; I long like St. Ignatius of Antioch to be crushed by the teeth of beasts, in order to become a bread worthy of God. With St. Agnes and St. Cecilia I would present my neck to the sword of the executioners; and, like Joan of Arc at the burning stake, murmur the name of Jesus."

In spite of these wild aspirations, she contented herself with the merest crumbs of humiliation, such as to be unjustly accused of breaking a vase and calmly not refuting it, refusing to complain when the old nun who shared with her some specially provided cider drank the lot, or eating meekly scraps which had been so often reheated they were like pieces of wood—the kitchen sisters knew little Thérèse would take no notice.

Not too difficult, all these small things? Well, there would be sharper trials in store, but, even so, to quote St. Thomas Aquinas: "Endurance is more difficult than aggression. . . . Endurance implies length of time, whereas aggression is con-

sistent with sudden movements; and it is more difficult to remain unmoved for a long time than to be moved suddenly to
something arduous."

*"Comme elle est mâle et virile! C'est 'un grand homme' dont
toute la doctrine prêche le renoncement"* (Her strength is that
of a man—a great man, whose entire doctrine preaches self-
denial), proclaimed Pope Pius XI at her canonization.

But we are anticipating. As yet she is still the rather gauche
postulant, a girl in her teens merely, barely out of childhood,
falling asleep over her prayers.

It was at about this time she was drawn to the devotion of
the Holy Face. This cultus, which was much encouraged at
the Lisieux Carmel, had been brought thither by Mother Geneviève from the Carmel at Tours, where a certain Sister Marie
de Saint-Pierre had received divine intimations on the subject.

It linked up in her case, as we shall see, with Thérèse's love
for her father; psychologists might say it had started from
there.

Sister Agnes' painting, a representation of the passion-stained
face of Jesus at the time of His crucifixion, taken either from
the Veil of Veronica or the Shroud of Turin, hung in the convent chapel. Her Lord, His comeliness blackened and broken
into ghastly holes exuding blood and sweat, glistened down
upon her with such a terrible expression of anguished yearning that she was beside herself to discover the means to console
Him.

"Souls!—souls, by the cross!" It was the only way. As she
had announced at the conventual examination on her arrival,
she had come to Carmel to pray for souls, particularly priests.
That was what her mortifications were about. If you picked up
a pin out of love you might save a soul. Later she would be
granted permission to add to her present name that of the
suffering Christ, and would sign herself Thérèse of the Child
Jesus of the Holy Face.

2

It is now that the mystery of her childhood vision among the homely shrubs and flowers of Les Bussonnets begins to reveal itself. It was a type of the agony in the garden, with Monsieur Martin representing the suffering Lord.

One day, when they were all children at Lisieux, their father had returned from a trip to Alençon in a state of troubled ecstasy. Whilst praying in the Church of Notre Dame he had become aware of "such graces, such untold consolation," that he had breathed out the following prayer: "My God, it is too much—I am too happy. It is impossible to reach Heaven in this way; I must suffer something for Thee! I offer myself as . . ."

The final word had been uttered in silence, but Thérèse knew now with the most terrible undeniable certainty what that word had been. He had offered himself as a "victim of holocaust." The divine fire was even now consuming him, in the form of *arterio sclerosis*. This dreadful, humiliating disease was gradually reducing her beloved father, he who had always been so exceptionally clear-minded and alert, he who had carried himself with the dignified upright bearing of a soldier, to a broken shell, a mere husk of a man.

The mind was already beginning to deteriorate, showing itself in periods of aberration, as when he neglected to feed his parrot so that it died, and, an instance far worse in its anxiety for Céline and Léonie, his sudden disappearance from the rustic bench on the lawn where they had placed him to enjoy the sunshine, to be found four days later wandering about the docks of Le Havre in a state of mental somnambulism. In a little over a year he would be removed to an asylum at Caen, a paralyzed imbecile.

While enduring the unutterable sorrow of this prodigious tragedy, Thérèse, by an extraordinary reversal of the will which lesser spirits might have termed heartless, was able to thank God for bestowing such a wonderful grace upon her family.

One would have thought that her being might have begun to disintegrate under the twisting sharpness of such a sacrifice. It probably did, in the natural sense. Supernaturally, it was a fresh source of life to her soul.

She knelt before the Holy Face, recognizing in its stricken lineaments the ravaging of her father as well as her God. Remembering the cauled figure passing between the fir-trees at Les Buissonnets, she thought of the face of Jesus "as it were, hidden and despised."

"Surely he hath borne our griefs, and carried our sorrows: yet we did esteem Him stricken, smitten of God, and afflicted.

But He was wounded for our transgressions, He was bruised for our iniquities. . . .

He was oppressed, and He was afflicted, yet He opened not his mouth. . . ."

Her father's compact had been sealed. A time for weeping? It was a time to rejoice!

She began to prepare for the ceremony of her Clothing with a new access of beating zeal.

CHAPTER FOUR

✿

Betrothed

I

FROM BEHIND THE shut door of the sewing-room at the top of the house an intriguing rhythmic noise is issuing. It rattles on blithely for a few minutes—stops—then starts again.

Hop-hop-hop-hop-hop! Pause. Then off it goes again, quicker than a bird. Hop-hop-hop-hop-hop-hop-hop! . . .

"Listen! She's been at it since early morning."

Sister Marthe of Jesus, unable to say nothing any longer, ceases her own noise of broom-knocking and looks at Sister Thérèse with an expression of communicating excitement.

The two postulants have been sent to tidy the attic. Thérèse returns her companion's speaking glance with a smile, the forefinger of her hand clasping a duster raised restrainingly to her lips. But it is no good. Having once broken silence, Sister Marthe will not be hushed.

"Oh, do let us go and take a peep at it—just one!"

Thérèse, half won over, shakes her head.

The quick-stamping foot of the sewing-machine—for that is the cause of Sister Marthe's wellnigh uncontainable agitation—stops and starts again.

"Please, Sister!"

Suddenly, with that slightly disconcerting decisiveness contingent to the putting away of scruples, Thérèse drops her duster, and gives Sister Marthe a little good-natured push in the direction she wishes to go.

The two girls cross the landing and knock on the opposite door, but the vociferous machine is at that moment in full spate, so they must enter without being asked.

A stuffy smell compounded of years of hot pressing-irons, beeswax, and machine oil . . . a little winter star of sunshine jumping up and down on the metal claw . . . Sister Marie of St. Joseph's sandals rising and falling on the treadle . . . and a great spread of folded whiteness like a slipping coverlet of snow.

The queer twisted nun with her pale clenched face does not look up immediately, but a flick of her lids reveals she is conscious of their presence.

Sister Marthe draws an ecstatic intake, and joins her hands in a silent clap. Thérèse sparkles too, her curved mouth twitching, then, like a sun-break, the famous smile in all its dazzling fullness.

The wizened nun pausing to nick a thread with big scissors almost shut, the three figures are suspended for a fraction of a second, held in *tableau.*

Beyond the small window the vein-like twigs of the tops of the chestnuts against a cold clear sky the blue of a bowl of frozen milk. A speck of swansdown from the fluffy coil on the table floats up into a thin sun-shaft. There is a spill of little pearls among pins. A fashion-plate with Paris written on it—what can that be doing in a Carmel?—rests beneath a scribble of tape-measure. Over the back of a chair hangs a web of white roses.

But, oh, that creamy avalanche of velvet, its ripple-edges bloomed with blur of light! What dazzling garment is in process of being evolved from it?

A wedding-dress? . . .

2

A few days later . . .

The most unlikely tradesmen are calling at the turn . . . the man from the *pâtisserie,* the boy from the toy shop, the young lady from the milliners, and lastly—this is surely rather

surprising—the drayman from the wine merchant's. His pack-
age, a wooden crate protruding whiskers of straw, is too large
to be inserted, and Sister Jeanne d'Arc, polishing chalices and
monstrances and the various-shaped glass coffers containing
sacred chips of labelled bones in the Sacristy, has to be summoned by the little wire-jerked bell to open the door.

She pops down her veil, and scurries off like anything rather
than her namesake, like an excited mouse to be exact.

Of all things—a case of champagne!

The bluff, moustached drayman makes a joke about it, and
even has to put a booted masculine foot inside the enclosure
to lower the box into the passage.

It is another present from Monsier Martin, as is the oval-
shaped parcel from the toyshop which, when the brown paper
is removed, reveals a huge melon, emerald green and mottled
with scarlet. There is a slip of paper attached. It is a most extraordinary piece of fruit, made of cardboard by the look of it.
You have to apply a match to its stalk, when there will follow
a minor explosion (very minor, one hopes!) and a shower of
bon-bons will burst into the air!

The emissary from the *pâtisserie* has delivered gingerbread
—brown and crumby and gilded, stamped with a big square
picture of two hares hanging up among vines and flowers, with
a gun on a table underneath—this from Madame Guérin.

But what on earth can a milliner have for a Carmel?

Purple tissue is whisked away, and there, fit for a princess
one might say, lies a wreath of buckram arum lilies. How
vividly green the twining leaves, how paint-pot bright the
yellow stamens, how dazzling white the curled-back cones.
They might have been freshly gathered that morning, everybody agrees, discountenancing the faint odor of glue. There is
a little gilt-edged card. *To our Darling Cousin Thérèse from
Jeanne and Marie, for her Clothing,* it says in correct and
scrupulous copper-plate, although childhood nerves have

wobbled occasionally. Her Clothing—so that is what all the fuss is about.

And what of her who is about to be clothed?

There are three days to go, and she is confined to her cell making her preliminary retreat. It is part of the Rule that a postulant shall at this time remain apart from the community, seeing only, for instruction, on each of the three days, either the Mother Prioress or the Mistress of the Novices. By an exceptional permission, probably because of her extreme youth and the delicacy of her religious sensibilities, Thérèse was allowed to unburden herself in writing to her two natural sisters.

The letters make poignant reading. Jesus seemed asleep, or if He woke it was only to pierce his "little ball" with innumerable pin-pricks.

When she paid her daily visit to Mother Marie Gonzague, always excessively preoccupied with the affairs of the convent, the consolation of being able to talk about her spiritual difficulties was marred by continual interruptions.

While recognizing the goodness of her fellows, she began to develop a loathing for them as creatures. "There is a touch of something in them that repels me! . . ." It seemed very uncharitable, but that was honestly what she felt and it would have been hypocritical to pretend otherwise.

Dryness was reducing her to a heap of dust, from which desolate condition she felt she had nothing to offer Her Lord.

"Very well, then," she wrote to Sister Agnes, "I will give Him that nothing!"

It must have been dreadful for a girl of sixteen, whose nerves, even in the comfortable surroundings of her home, had been often exacerbated, to be shut away in the claustrophobic dimensions of that cold stark cell, awaiting the awful moment of final renunciation without a particle of sweetness to give the sacrifice a meaning.

But she held on. She even referred to her condition as peaceful, but it must have been a most dubious peace. And all the

time she hugged the suffering to her heart, thanked her remorseless God for it, in a way that in another, less dedicated,
soul would have been dangerously like the perverseness of
insanity.

She believed it was Jesus' way of detaching her from everything that was not Himself.

"If you knew how great is my joy," she sang like a bird
on a thorn, "at having no joy . . . it is essence of joy (but
wholly unfelt)." A strange joy, surely, seemingly compounded
of unutterable woes? We would have to be saints ourselves to
completely understand it.

And on top of everything else He sent her one of His
typical delays.

She had been looking forward to her reception on the 9th
January, as that would be exactly nine months after her entry,
but Monseigneur Hugonin found he would be unable to pre-
side until a day later. That nine months represented to her the
period of gestation of the infant Jesus in the womb of the
Blessed Virgin. Admittedly, as the Clothing represented her
betrothal, she had rather anticipated the facts of this conjugal
analogy; nevertheless, it was still an irritating disappointment.

She went on waiting in the darkness. All that could be said
was that the darkness was luminous.

On the last evening she sent a simple little note, so char-
acteristically disarming, to Sister Agnes again, asking her if,
as a commemorative present, she would like to give her her
Chinese ink and gold leaf, and "Will you please slip open
our door at six if you're there, otherwise I must wake myself
up," adding "If all these things are a nuisance, don't give me
anything. I can very well do without."

3

The weather is suddenly so mild it is like a foretaste of
spring. Because she loved that pure fragile element whose

starry flakes were, like herself, the flowers of winter, she had hoped it would snow; but there was no possibility of that now.

The Church of Carmel, open to the public, is fairly full.

Nuns, like criminals, are easily forgotten once they are shut away behind their bars, but there were many in Lisieux who still bore in mind the grave yet vivacious little girl with the wonderful golden ringlets, whom they had watched grow up from a wide-eyed toddler grasping its father's big hand to a smart young lady at the beginning of her teens, setting off to interview a Bishop, the famous hair no longer flowing behind her like a mane of fire but coiled up neatly into a discreet inconspicuous bun. And now they had gathered, not to see that hair cut off, for that would be done in private, but to glimpse the complete creature for the last time. After her brief appearance today she will be seen no more by the eyes of the world.

Her aunt and uncle and two cousins, with young Doctor La Néele, occupy special *prie-Dieu* arranged directly in front of the altar-rail.

Monsieur Martin, walking with some difficulty on two sticks, shepherded by Léonie and Céline, has gone to take his place near the door of the enclosure. The change in him is painfully noticeable; the effort he is making to seem alert and upright increases his pathetic appearance. Is it the emotion of the occasion or the steadily gaining palsy which is causing his muscles to jerk in this distressing manner? Alas, it is only too evidently the latter. He looks so stooping, so rheumy, so really old, it is tragic. The eyeballs, no longer clear and twinkling, are yellowish suffused with pink, containing an expression of such overpowering struggle between the clay and the light that it is almost unbearable to look at him. But prayer triumphs. Light is the conqueror, if only for today.

The small dark door, heavy with ominousness, opens quite simply—such a little ordinary door, but separating two kingdoms—and she is before him.

The community, clustering behind her, wave *au revoir* till the leaf closes upon her.

"Ah! here is my little Queen."

She flings herself into her father's embrace, exhaling a fullness of heart whose intensity words would be inadequate to describe. Then, detaching herself to kiss Céline and Léonie, she draws back to display her finery.

Tears must be withheld at all costs. We must not be sad now. She is too lovely. Everything has been done to enhance her beauty, as much as if she were a young bride of the world. Her fabulous hair has been tonged by the *coiffeur*. She has bathed in rainwater dashed with eau-de-cologne. And her dress (we can only imagine it—it was cut up later for vestments) a dream of creamy velvet and lace and swansdown such as to set the heart of any maiden palpitating, has been executed from the latest fashion-plates of Paris.

It is a charming period. The bustle has gone. The line is simple and unexaggerated, merely stressing the natural curves of femininity. The bodice, narrow-waisted as when a flower-cup joins the stem, with its high neck and pointed front, is decorated with rose motifs of Alençon and a line of pearls for buttons. The oval yoke of marabout dips across her bosom, and there are three bands of marabout encircling the foot of the bell-shaped rose-appliquéd skirt. Her sleeves are tight, lace over chiffon, concluding like mittens on the backs of her hands. The sloping shoulders carry knots of satin ribbon, and there is a wider ribbon sash, folded and draped across her hips, fastening in a huge rosette in the small of her back. Tiny pearly-centered rosettes complete the elegance of her crêpe-de-chine slippers with their fashionable Louis heels. She is crowned with the wreath of artificial lilies, but a sheaf of real ones, odoriferous trumpets with enormous golden-pollened stamens, rests in the crook of one arm. Her long tulle veil floats crisply about her as if it were painted on the air.

Moving, solemn yet smiling, up the aisle on the black sleeve

of her father—it is she really who is supporting him—to
where her invisible bridegroom awaits her through the open
gates of the altar-rail, the slightly stuffy atmosphere of the
church, laminated with wax droppings and stale incense, eddies
with hardly-suppressed exclamations.

"Regardez-la!"

"Elle a l'air d'un ange!"

"Charmante! . . ."

"La petite Reine!"

Mass. Holy Communion.

The Bishop, preceded by the acolyte, carrying the cross, and
the company of priests, leads her, followed by her relatives,
back to the enclosure door.

Heart-stricken farewells, mercifully formalized, not to be
lingered over, the door opens, and she is back inside.

The great black curtain over the grille has been flung aside,
so we are able to watch.

They sing in Latin a verse of a hymn, which may be translated as follows—it is very lovely:

> "O Glorious One of the Virgins,
> Sublime among the stars,
> He who created thee,
> Did as a little one
> Suck milk from thy breast."

Then, in a fit of absentmindedness, the Bishop began to in
tone the *Te Deum.* One of the clergy whispered a reminder
that this great hymn of thanksgiving was only sung at a Profession. Even so, the hymn was continued to the end.

The whole community, their veils down, lighted candles in
hand, bear her to the choir. She kneels, and kisses the brass
feet of the crucifix.

But suddenly there is something repugnant to the senses in
this melancholy file of faceless creatures, creatures no more it
would seem, rather black piles of shuffling dust. Strange un-

earthly voices issue from invisible mouths, bodiless, thin, concerted to one weird cry of piercing unbearable sweetness.

And that lovely shining girl in their midst about to be stifled, quenched, as they, beneath the heavy garments of renunciation.

But it has not been designed to appeal to the senses.

The above is how we see it who know little or nothing beyond the joys of the flesh. Morbid? It could be. It is not. We have learned as much as that. The risk is terrifying. The reward?

"Eye hath not seen, nor ear heard, neither have entered into the heart of man, the things which God hath prepared for them that love him."

But Thérèse did not forget that His love was gratuitous, given to thieves and prostitutes and nuns alike.

The Bishop, back in the Sanctuary, conducts his part from there. She kneels. He speaks to her through the bars.

"What do you ask?"

"The mercy of God, the poverty of the Order, and the company of the sisters."

"Is it of your own free will and your own accord that you wish to take the religious habit?"

"Yes."

"Will you constantly persevere in the Order until Death?"

"Yes."

"Will you keep these things for the sole love of Our Lord?"

"Yes, with the Grace of God and the prayers of the sisters."

She rises, and two nuns take her away.

When she returns the princess garments have vanished. She is a little brown Cinderella, a Carmelite.

Meanwhile the Cloak, the Scapular, the Cincture, disposed on a stool near the grating, have been blessed.

The 113th Psalm is intoned, concluding with the significant verse:

"He maketh the barren woman to keep house, and to be a joyful mother of children. Praise ye the Lord."

The children of little Thérèse are now too numerous to begin to count. . . .

The Bishop says:

"May the Lord clothe thee with the new man, who was created according to God in justice and sanctity of Truth."

The nuns put on the Cincture.

"When thou wast younger, thou didst gird thyself, and didst walk where thou wouldst, but when thou shalt be old, another shall gird thee."

The Scapular is placed over her head.

"Receive the sweet yoke of Christ, and His light burden."

The white Cloak is hung about her shoulders.

"They that follow the lamb without spot, shall walk with Him in white: therefore let thy garment be ever white, as a sign of inward purity."

The nuns begin to chant the hymn *Veni Creator Spiritus*, and Mother Marie Gonzague takes Thérèse by the hand, leading her to the middle of the choir.

She is to be crucified in type upon a cross of flowers.

A strip of scarlet baize has been unrolled upon the stones, bordered with potted plants. Palms like green bird wings, misty pungent ferns, veined hairy coleuses, pink papery azaleas, wax-belled hyacinths, the variegated leaves and blossoms permeate the surrounding air with breaths of fragrance.

She prostrates herself obediently in their midst for the space of the seven stanzas, her face inclined on the red pathway, her outstretched fingers shadowed by petals and fronds.

Rising, she is dashed with Holy Water—the divine refreshment for the flower which is herself—then taken by the Prioress to the choir altar, she kneels and kisses it in token of her submission.

A tall candle, painted with gilt and roses, is placed in her hand, and she makes her way between the files of *religieuses*, giving and receiving from each one the embrace of sisterhood, as they sing together:

"Behold how good and how pleasant it is: for brethren to dwell together in unity."

Piles of dust? Oh no, we were mistaken!—merely temporarily frightened, like children, by the black veils. Even taciturn Sister Marie of St. Joseph smiles on this occasion. The effect is of some quietly happy family rejoicing at the inclusion of a new member.

When she comes to Sister Marie and Sister Agnes she does her best to make no difference, but inevitably there is a slight private satisfaction—it would not be human otherwise—as, for a brief moment, she is clasped in the arms of her own flesh. She desires, in the earthly sense, only one more thing—that Céline shall eventually join them.

Then, as they file out of the stalls and pass through the cloisters back to the main building, something wonderful happens. A miracle? Perhaps. There are days when everything seems a miracle. Her secret wish—it had hardly been a prayer —is suddenly granted.

The gravel of the quadrangle is being slowly sprinkled with delicate confetti of snow. . . .

CHAPTER FIVE

❄

Springtime

I

THE SPRING COMES to the earth year after year, but it is always
for the first time. It is as common as babies, but as all mothers
know there has never been anything quite like a new child.
The petals, the dews, the fragrant cleanness and freshness,
memory cannot sully them, cannot really contribute.

It is the first time, the jonquil has opened her golden eye.
We have never seen the jewel-purple of these violets before,
never yet heard the water-trill of these birds, never breathed
such green-scented aid, nor responded, like the buds, to the
warm caress of just this sun. The curtain of time is torn apart
and we have stepped into the eternal Eden-world of the first
spring.

It is spring in the garden of Carmel.

Sister Thérèse, darning altar-linen in the grotto of St. Mary
Magdalen, praises God in the prospect. "Behold, He shall
make all things new."

A blackbird practicing roulades on a bouncing spray shakes
down diamonds and pink snow of prunus. There was a soft
shower earlier this morning. The air is being pierced by little
chirping violins and piccolos, but we do not know where they
are. A whole orchestra of sounds is tuning up.

The first weak bees, seeming still a little exhausted, like
the uncreasing leaves, crawl in and out the colored cups and
tassels, the trumpets of the flowers, the primulas, the pink
currants, the daffodils—but why name them? They are opening
around us as thick and ubiquitous as to be *pointilliste,* but in
a perfect rhythm, no quicker than nature intended, slow accord-

ing to our reckoning perhaps, for the plants do not jerk forward according to seconds and minutes—they have no need to hurry.

Fortunate you who have caught a glimpse of the raising of a petal eyelid! . . . But who has heard the silent explosions on these boughs of blossom?—they are not here, and then they are. Yesterday unnoticed, today a new constellation. The earth is breaking into stars.

And the stars are in our blood. It is more than a little disturbing, even painful. One may be rather tired in the spring. Gradually we lift up our faces to the sun.

She said: "I dare to gaze upon the divine sun of love, and I burn to dart upwards to Him! . . . What is to become of me? . . . Must I die of sorrow because of my helplessness? Oh no! With daring self-abandonment there will I remain until death, my gaze fixed upon that divine sun." And in another place: "Let us be made golden by the sun of His love."

But it is not yet the ripening, the burning, the sun over the harvest. Not yet the consuming holocaust. It is still the spring. She is not yet seventeen. Difficult to realize that when she is grave, as now, but at recreation when she laughs, and makes others laugh, there is no doubt of it.

Her needle pricks and flashes. Far off in the glitter the gardener is wheeling a barrow of geraniums to transplant in the borders. He has been remiss and only just pruned her beloved chestnuts—our chestnuts, she should say. Their lopped arms lie on the ground. So charming their fans of new leaves, comically up-and-down like donkey's ears. She had felt very cross with him, so hurt to see them severed when the sap was rising. The alley seemed quite spoiled. Then she had thought if they had belonged to another Carmel far away she would not have been aware. It was a way of looking at it. In that case there would have been no disagreeable feelings, so why indulge them now? She forgave him, was sorry to have been so un-mortified.

She was still very dry, the spring had not come to her parched soul. There seemed no supernatural spring, as yet.

Jesus was still asleep. She continued to fall asleep herself. After Holy Communion she would return to her place, and almost immediately her head would begin nodding. Sometimes she felt obliged to continue her thanksgiving all day to make up for it. At first it had worried her, but now she was resigned. It was merely the frailty of the flesh. Did not mesmerists and surgeons put their patients to sleep while they effected their cures? Perhaps that was what God was doing with her? Anyway, she knew He would love her just as much asleep as awake.

Last month a strange thing had happened. She had gone about her duties for a whole week in a kind of trance. It would have been impossible to explain her feelings. For once her soul had been lapped about with an extraordinary supernatural peace, a kind of quietly ecstatic well-being in which she had moved like an angel, nothing to do with the contrived willed happiness she was used to, but a gift from heaven, a kind of golden perfumed cloud from which she had performed her allotted tasks without effort, almost unconsciously. Was it the blessed condition her great mother Teresa had referred to in her mystic treatise? But she had been a saint. . . .

Oh, but it had not lasted! It would have been too much. She was so earthbound, worse, for the natural beauty surrounding her seemed, today, unable to touch her. Yet how lovely the japonica was, its coral-red blossoms decorating the doorway . . . the blue of the sky intense beyond them. It reminded her of the japonica in the garden at home, the thick screen of it on the trellis before the wash-house.

And now there would be no one to see it. Les Buissonnets was deserted. A month after her Clothing Monsieur Martin had had to be removed to a private asylum at Caen, and Léonie and Céline had gone with him; and after their return to board with the Guérins until finding another house, the furniture of their home, with all its endearing associations, would be dispersed too. It would come back to Les Buissonnets, but not for many years.

They lived now in the hospital annexe with the nuns, the ship-hatted sisters of St. Vincent de Paul.

She thought of her poor father dependent on strangers, the increasing indignities to which he would be subjected, however kindly. It was terrible. It was the cross. She thanked God for it.

The thing to do was to try to forget her own sorrow in comforting Céline, and of course Léonie. Mother Marie Gonzague had, in the circumstances, given her special permission to write.

Before their father had become too ill to understand, Céline had managed to tell him that one day she too desired to join her sister in Carmel—but when that will be is now very uncertain.

Thérèse's letters to her, and to others, are often very quaint, and they nearly always seem to be written in haste, as if she were afraid of indulging her feelings too much; or perhaps it was a subconscious longing to be off—she is continually referring to the shortness of this life—"An instant between two eternities."

The bell rings, and she leaves off her "cat-scratch," as she calls it, in the middle of a word. The practice of obedience will do more in the way of helping her correspondents than any writing she might have sent. Once she was so poor her ink was almost gone, so she spat into the ink-well to eke it out.

In the mixing of metaphors she has a style all her own. It is the result, doubtless, of her spontaneous enthusiasm. Lilies become lambs, the lambs grow wings, then turn into grains of sand! But when she has advice to convey, or is answering an appeal, her expressions are vividly apposite and direct. Later, as we shall see, her letters to her missionary friend, the Abbé Bellière, are models of charm, subtlety, and infinite wisdom.

Her close relationship with Céline, her "other self," reveals itself most poignantly in their correspondence. Thérèse was yearning for the day when the enclosure door would open to admit her third sister, the one perhaps she loved best of all, but she knew that for the time being it was Céline's duty to remain with their father. It would not have been fair to leave Léonie to carry the full weight of that adored, yet agonizing, burden.

She was found of Léonie too, but it is very obvious that even Thérèse, with her clear insight into human nature and pity for its frailty, was unable to embrace this odd one without a certain reservation. One's sympathies rush inevitably to the side of Léonie. "She is less fortunate than we, Jesus has given her less," remarked Thérèse.

But was she correct? Léonie has not been canonized, but the more one thinks of her and her peculiar odyssey, which in the end did bring her into the haven of the religious life—though perhaps it was never a haven for her?—the more one is drawn to her in a way which is mysterious. Her sanctity was obscure, perhaps hidden even deeper than her illustrious sister's, but it was there. Will she at some not too distant day be elevated to a position of honor on the Church's altars, with a message of hope for the misunderstood? It may be so. She is not easy to put out of mind.

Meantime Thérèse continued to encourage Céline to endure her cross and to regard it as a blessing. They had a queer way of looking at things, these Martins—queer, that is, to us who cannot refrain from a certain squeamishness in our attitude to suffering. "My Céline's dream is very lovely," comments the saint, and we glance at the footnote to discover she had dreamed she was being martyred! No end could be better, one supposes. But "lovely"? . . . Well, it is possible. In dealing with saints it is necessary to readjust our values.

There was an almost psychic link between these two girls. They might have been twins. On one occasion it was necessary for Céline to go to a ball. It was after she and Léonie had returned to Lisieux. It was, no doubt, a perfectly harmless affair, rather stuffy if we know anything of the social round of small-town communities. Certainly Céline, along with her two cousins, would be heavily chaperoned by Madame Guérin. But Thérèse was a little doubtful. She knew it was precarious for a girl with a religious vocation to indulge herself in the amusements of the world. She prayed. . . .

A young man—we do not know who; perhaps his bourgeois politeness served only to disguise the makings of a rake—requested the pleasure of a dance. Céline complied, only to discover that the moment she and her partner took up their positions on the floor they were unable to move! Uncanny, and considerably embarrassing. What ludicrous effect these two stuck figures must have created in the eyes of the spectators we will leave to the reader's imagination. Enough to say that Céline sat out for the rest of the evening, and Thérèse, when her sister came to the convent parlor to give an account of these extraordinary proceedings, expressed a complacent, but no doubt well-intentioned, relief!

But we must be careful of sniggering. Perhaps there really was more in it than appeared on the surface. Perhaps if they had been permitted to dance a chain of events would have been started which would have resulted in—what? The loss of a soul? It could be so. We are always in danger if we choose to think about it. In another way we are always quite safe. . . .

2

It was at about this time that Thérèse was able to come to the aid of her cousin, Marie Guérin, in a way that, instead of disconcerting, provided a reassuring and comforting solution to a young girl's problems. Marie Guérin had reached that disturbing time in a maiden's life when the warm nights of spring caused her to sit up in bed in the passionate moonlight, her

face white and luminous as the orb staring in at her through
the window, her taut arms clasped about her knees, for there
was nothing else to hug, her blood moving and coagulating
in her veins in an aberrant way which was at the same time
both delicious and frightening.

It is then that the adolescent body, tortured and bewildered,
in the grip of elemental forces stronger than the will, however
rigorously trained by parental and tutorial admonitions against
the flesh, seeks inevitably for any kind of relief which will
serve to assuage its trembling and longing. And the reaction is,
inevitably, a remorse which is probably even more painful,
being mental, than the previous physical distress.

We do not know for certain if this was the cause of the
child's feelings of guilt, but it might well have been so and
it will serve. Enough to say the pathetic young creature believed
she had done something unspeakable, and that she was in
a state of mortal sin. She was too ashamed and confused to
make a proper confession, and thus dare not go to Holy Communion.

She wrote to Thérèse. The reply came promptly. That peculiar psychic intuition of which she was possessed, and which
alway reminded her when someone she loved was in trouble,
had already rung its warning bell. She had expected Marie
was about to communicate with her, had had a dream to that
effect. She understood immediately.

". . . you have not committed the *shadow* of *sin*. I know so
well what temptations of this kind are, that I can give you the
assurance without fear; besides, Jesus tells me so in the depths
of my heart. . . . The devil must indeed be clever to deceive a
soul like that! . . . But, surely, you know, darling, that that is
the one goal of his desires. He realizes, treacherous creature
that he is, that he cannot get a soul to sin if that soul wants to
belong wholly to Jesus, so he only tries to make it *think* it is in
sin. It is already much for him to have put confusion into that
soul, but his rage demands something more; he wants to de-

prive Jesus of a loved tabernacle; since he cannot enter that sanctuary himself, he wants at least to have it remain *empty* and without master! . . .

"Alas! what will become of that poor heart? . . . When the devil has succeeded in keeping a soul away from Holy Communion, he has *gained all* . . . and Jesus weeps! . . . O my darling, do you realize that Jesus is there in the tabernacle expressly for you, for *you alone*, He burns with the desire to come into your heart . . . don't listen to the demon, laugh at him, and go without fear to receive the Jesus of peace and love! . . .

"But I hear you say: 'Thérèse says this because she does not know . . . and anyhow I cannot receive Communion, for I believe that I should be committing a sacrilege, etc. . . .' Yes, your poor little Thérèse does know, I tell you that she sees it all; she assures you that you can go without fear to receive your one true Friend. She also has passed through the martyrdom of scruples; but Jesus gave her the grace to receive Communion all the same, even at the time when she thought she had committed grave sins . . . so! I assure you that she realizes that it was the only way to get rid of the demon; for when he sees that he is wasting his time, he leaves you in peace! . . .

"No, it is not possible that a heart 'that finds no rest save in the sight of the tabernacle' should offend Jesus enough to be unfit to receive Him. What offends Jesus, what wounds His heart, is want of trust! . . .

"Your heart is made to love Jesus, to love Him passionately; pray hard that the most beautiful years of your life may not be spent in imaginary fears."

But despite these wise and heartfelt reassurances Marie continued to suffer. As Céline was more immediately available, and perhaps after a crisis when she could contain herself no longer, she spoke to her. But she found it necessary to write to Thérèse again.

This time the latter felt she would do well to consult Mother

Marie Gonzague, who must have had more experience in dealing with such problems. The Prioress—and those who have
remarked only her apparent severity might be persuaded to
remember this—had no compunction in dismissing the matter
as not being worth prolonged consideration. She instructed
Thérèse to write to her cousin to the effect that Marie had done
right in confiding in Céline, but that she would do better not
to converse of such things, dismissing them instantaneously
from her mind, for she was convinced she was doing no wrong.
No more mention seems to have been made of the subject, and
we may take it that henceforth, through the good offices of
her intercessor, the child was permitted to recover her peace
of mind.

Thus, despite her own suffering and aridity, the saint was
already beginning to do good to souls beyond the confines
of her hidden cell.

Her advice in the case of her cousin, no matter what might
have been the opinion of the prudish, was evidently right. In
1895, five years later, Marie Guérin was received into the
Carmel as a postulant. She died there, a fully professed nun,
on the 14th April, 1905.

CHAPTER SIX

❈

Married

I

IT IS THE evening of the 7th September, 1890. In a little while the bell will ring for Compline.

The mellow sunset of this time of the year flows over the Carmel like thick Normandy cider. A russet-glowing square edged with tips of leaves hangs on the whitewashed wall of Sister Thérèse's cell as if projected from a magic-lantern.

She watches it; the shadows of the ears of leaves move a little in the settling evening airs. . . .

Tomorrow she is to be fully professed, is to take her final vows.

Her preliminary retreat has been passed in that usual state of dryness which, if it were not so unutterably painful, would be beginning to seem a little ridiculous. Today has been awful. She has received news that her father is worse. The ceremony of Profession is private, so he would not have been able to attend in any case, but there is small consolation in that.

Her face is pressed and white with suffering, the eyes so shadowed and enormous as to appear deranged. Menstrual pains are adding a weight of physical depression to her spiritual torments. She feels she can make no more efforts. Staring dazedly at the square of sunshine on the wall, mouthing silently "Thy will be done . . ." she knows inevitably her endurance is at and end. The unrelieved darkness of soul in which she has moved for how long?—it seems an eternity—has brought her to the very verge of madness.

Any minute now a piercing hysterical shriek is likely to shatter the hellish silence, for that is what the quietness of the convent has become. It is finished. She can go no more.

Rising, she stands gripping the edge of the small deal table,

trying to bring back her whirling thoughts—they are like
wild careening birds who have been shut up too long.

There must be no scandal. Everything must be done me-
thodically and in good order until the very last. One thing
she is certain of. She has no vocation. Thank God, at least,
she has realized it in time.

Terrible alluring possibilities of a life in the world rear
up before her like obscenely painted screens hurried before
her eyes grinning devils. Gripping the rough wood harder,
she tries not to look. No, no, it must not be that, none of
those wickednesses!

She will go back and be a nurse to her father. She will live
quietly with Céline and Léonie. They will be pious old maids.
Good works, simplicity, peace. . . . The screens collapse and
clatter away into sulphurous darkness, the cries of the cha-
grined demons squawking like parrots in her clapped ears.

She shudders, and shakes. Calm—she must be calm. There
goes the bell. She must speak to Sister Marie of the Angels
before she goes into choir, tell her definitely but composedly
that having no vocation she must leave the convent at once.

A snail-track of cold sweat trickles down her side under
the thick serge. She grasps the latch, raises it resolutely, and
passes out on the stairs.

The whispering veils and sandals lisp around her on the
air and stones. She moves with them, but of them no more.

The bell has stopped now abruptly. Sister Marie of the
Angels has already taken up her position in the after-glow-
ing stalls.

What to do? If she does not tell someone at once she will
collapse. She hesitates, blown about by panic winds, then
rushes before her superior and beckons her out.

Sister Marie of the Angels puts down her missal, and joins
Thérèse in the cloisters. At first the poor girl is trembling
so much she cannot speak. The older nun grips her arm firmly
to steady her, but with great kindness.

"What is it, sister? Are you ill? Try to speak, my dear."

Thérèse looks up. Her wan face is more ludicrous than anything else.

"Sister, I have no vocation. It is definite. I must go away. I have no right here. I must go."

The Novice Mistress looks steadily at her for one second, and then quite simply, but no doubt inspired by God, for it is a precarious moment, her concerned expression breaks into a smile. She begins to laugh. Thérèse begins to laugh too.

"Quick, sister—we shall be late!—take your place in the choir. We will speak about it afterwards."

But afterwards there is nothing to speak about. It is thought necessary to mention the matter to the Prioress, but by then Thérèse does not require her reassurance.

It had been no more then the usual nerve-storm before a profession. Priests get it too, quite often, before taking their final vows. The devil's last desperate attempt. A laugh, and he had been vanquished!

Thérèse rests that night in a profound and dreamless sleep. In the morning—the bright day of her espousals at last—she awakes as refreshed, and happy, and confident, perhaps more so, than the most loved bride on earth.

In her autobiography she writes:

". . . my soul was flooded with heavenly joy, and in that peace 'which surpasseth understanding' I pronounced my holy vows. Many were the graces I asked, and feeling myself truly a 'Queen' I took advantage of my title to beg from the King all possible favors for His ungrateful subjects. No one was forgotten. I longed that every sinner on earth might be converted, all captive souls in Purgatory set free, and on my heart I bore this letter containing what I desired for myself:

"O Jesus, My Divine Spouse, grant that my baptismal robe may never be sullied. Take me from this world rather than allow me to stain my soul by committing the least wilful fault.

May I never seek or find ought but Thee alone! May all crea-
tures be as nothing to me and I as nothing to them! May no
earthly thing disturb my peace!

"*O Jesus, I ask for peace . . . peace, and above all,* LOVE *. . .*
love without limit. I ask that for Thy sake I may die a martyr—
give me martyrdom of soul or body. Or rather give me both.

"*Grant that I may fulfil my promises in all their perfection;*
that no one may think of me, that I may be forgotten and trod-
den underfoot as a grain of sand. I offer myself to Thee, O my
Beloved, that Thou mayest ever perfectly accomplish Thy
Holy Will in me without creatures placing any obstacle in the
way.

"When at the close of that glorious day I laid my crown
of roses, as was usual, at Our Lady's feet (it was the Feast
of the Nativity of Mary) it was without regret; I felt that
time could never take away my happiness."

2

Shortly after the Veiling, a seperate ceremony which took
place on the 24th September Monsieur Martin was again
too ill to be present—her cousin Jeanne was married to Doctor La Néele.

As may be imagined, there had been much preliminary
running to and fro between the Guérin drawing-room and
the Carmel parlor. An earthly wedding with all its human
implications, brought so near to the Community by reason
of its involving a relation of three of the sisters, quite naturally
set up a commotion among the Brides of Christ which did
them no harm, serving as an obvious outlet for that gossipy
femininity which no women ever quite renounces even if she
becomes a nun. We may be sure the "grape-vine" buzzed and
whispered with such intriguing bits of information as to the
merits of the bridegroom's physiognomy—was he dark or

fair, dashingly handsome, or dependent for his appeal on his good character only?—not to mention speculations as to the cost and items of the brides trousseau, her *dot,* who had given what in the way of wedding presents, and if the surroundings for the honeymoon were to be suitably idyllic.

We do not know where they went; perhaps it was to the chateau at La Musse, a small country estate left to the Guérins by Madame Guérin's recently deceased brother. The family, while never actually taking up residence there, was in the habit of using the property for holidays—Thérèse used to request her cousin Marie to bring back moss and bark for the nuns to make into boxes and cribs and other articles of piety. Wooded, private, with a slight ostentation about it, it sounds just the place for a young highly respectable married couple of the bourgeoisie to retire to.

Soon after their return, her connubial bliss glowing upon her like the bloom on one of the conservatory peaches, Jeanne made her excited yet complacent way to the Carmel parlor to tell Thérèse all about it—well, not perhaps all, but enough to convey how pleasurable it was to be married.

She was full of her husband. Thérèse listened, interestedly at first, then patiently. Her immediate reaction on hearing so much of the delights of conjugal intimacy, the breakfast kisses, the competition to please each other, how amusing, how clumsy, how little-boyish men were, even if in the eyes of the world they appeared as rising members of a profession as serious-minded as medicine—her immediate reaction to all this bird-chatter of enthusiasm was one of very human envy.

How lovely if she could have welcomed her Lord home every evening, brought forward warmed slippers, ladled out potage for Him of her own making, like the glitter-eyed young matron at the other side of the grille. She saw the absurdity of such an idea immediately, but if one could be simple enough, was it not also charming?

Thérèse, despite her unsentimental intelligence, was not

afraid of sentiment. Those who see her in terms of crystallized rose leaves have mistaken the submission which kept her in such close contact with the behavior of ordinary people for mere lisping gush. But the positive antinomies of humility and magnanimity walked either side of her soul like guardian angels. She had no fear of appearing foolish.

When Jeanne, with her affecting mixture of staidness and enthusiasm, her little basket and jingling chatelaine, had taken herself off, Thérèse set herself to thinking in what way she might draw level with her cousin's so justifiable pride in a good husband.

Her sense of humor gave her an idea.

Taking a freshly sharpened quill and a piece of the expensive pasteboard used for the writing of saleable texts, she composed the following, in honor of her own Spouse, and for the diversion of the novices:

"GOD ALMIGHTY, Creator of Heaven and Earth, Sovereign Ruler of the Universe, and the MOST GLORIOUS VIRGIN MARY, Queen of the Heavenly court, announce to you the Spiritual Espousals of Their August Son, JESUS, King of Kings, and Lord of Lords, with little THÉRÈSE Martin, now Princess and Lady of His Kingdoms of the Holy Childhood and the Passion, assigned to her in dowry by her Divine Spouse, from which Kingdoms she holds her titles of nobility—OF THE CHILD JESUS AND OF THE HOLY FACE. It was not possible to invite you to the Wedding Feast which took place on the Mountain of Carmel, September 8th, 1890—the Heavenly Court was alone admitted—but you are requested to be present at the At Home which will take place tomorrow, the Day of Eternity, when Jesus, the Son of God, will come in the Clouds of Heaven, in the splendor of His Majesty, to judge the living and the dead. The hour being uncertain, you are asked to hold yourselves in readiness and to watch."

✻

CHAPTER SEVEN

Thérèse, Mistress of the Novices

I

IN THE CONVENTUAL elections of 1893 Sister Agnes, by a narrow margin, was voted Mother Superior, and Mother Marie Gonzague removed for the time being to the position of Mistress of the Novices.

In actual fact it was Sister Thérèse who was given the work to do, but for some reason—maybe it was a sop thrown to Mother Marie's *amour propre*—the honor of the name went to the previous Prioress.

It was just another of those pin-picking slights which Thérèse was by this time resigned to. She had not yet reached the stage when she would welcome them. Eventually she would arrive at a state of complete indifference as far as the actions of creatures were concerned. But, in any case, it always suited her better to have to reconcile herself to a certain amount of misunderstanding, so she did not feel she had any cause for complaint.

On the contrary, her embarrassment arose from the thought of the high practical responsibility of directing souls, a much more important task than the bearing of a mere title. She was not at all convinced of her suitability. As was usual in all undertakings, serious or small, she placed the full incumbency on Almighty God.

She became a child again. Indeed, she had always had a great reluctance to grow up. That she was a sort of female Peter Pan would be a good line for her detractors!

Nestling in her Father's arms she asked only that He should

supply the grain for her little chicks, and she would scatter it without even turning her head.

One gathers she did the scattering with considerable circumspection, although she maintained she threw it heedlessly, and that the results were sometimes clearly productive and sometimes quite unnoticeable; but one has only to see the effect of her teaching on her children today, when she is no longer here in a physical sense, to realize how powerful her influence must have been when she moved among her pupils with all the magnetism of her many-faceted personality in constant play.

She was like an ember. The Spirit blew on her and she glowed, and touched off holy fires in others; yet many of the community, even after seeing her lit, as it were, as quickly forgot, and thought of her as in no way outstanding.

It makes a curious paradox, this soul that shone out like a jewel and then was as suddenly veiled and hidden. Perhaps it was because she was emptied of self, like a glass, and then God poured in His wine . . . it was drunk, and the glass remained empty again. She admitted that Grace was apportioned out to her only as she required it; she carried no stock.

She realized most people's problems amounted to the same thing in the end, but that every soul must be guided to a solution individually—there was to be no hard and fast system. It was her Little Way; once its followers had accepted their smallness, and knew that they of themselves could do nothing, but that if they abandoned themselves to Him, God could, and would, do all—once they had accepted these simple tenents, then their unique paths branched off more numerous and diverse than the tributary streams of the sea.

But she was no quietist. One had still to be making efforts.

If anything she erred on the side of severity, for she knew it was fatal to counteract a reprimand by any condoning softness once the recipient was hurt. In a combat she could have wished to have been spared, her thrusts were "the wounds of a friend," and any alleviation would deter their purgative blood-letting.

No, it was not easy for her to be fierce. She knew that for "a reprimand to be fruitful, it must cost in the giving; and it must be given without a movement of passion in the heart." She admitted she would rather receive a thousand reproaches herself than address to another a single one.

"We must not let kindness degenerate into weakness," she said. "When we have blamed justly we ought to leave it so, and not yield to feelings of distress at having given pain and caused tears. To run after the aggrieved one and console her is to do more harm than good. To leave her to herself is to force her to expect nothing from creatures, to have recourse to the good God, to see her failings, and to humble herself."

But she assumed no superiority. She was her pupil's "servant," and when congratulated by one of them on the importance and honor of her position as directress, asked merely why it should be thought that her happiness consisted in that, for it seemed to her of little consequence to whom should be assigned the task of distributing instruction when the inspiration came from God.

She tried to make them see that she was no better than they, that no one, by his or her own merits, was any better than anyone else. She herself admitted to all the temptations they confessed to her, and would go to the most subtle and, in some opinions, perhaps even dangerous lengths to win their confidence; such as pretending on one occasion that she felt lukewarm and half-hearted in order to excite zeal in another.

Sometimes she appeared to contradict herself. Why not? It was a very human characteristic. And scripture itself is composed of balancing paradoxes. But if that had been pointed out to her it is unlikely she would have offered it as an excuse —she never excused herself for anything—rather would she have admitted it to be a fault, and thus climbed another step down into the "fertile valley of humiliation."

For example (let us hope these admonitions were not administered to the same novice!), she issued a curt reprimand to one who was going slowly to the laundry: "Is that how one hastens who has children to nourish, and who is obliged to work for their living?" Then, later: "You are too much absorbed in your work . . . you give yourself up too much to what you do . . . you ought to be detached from your personal work, employing therein conscientiously the time appointed, but with disengagement of heart." It may be remarked, she was never seen to hurry herself.

But however exacting she may have seemed at times, it was a sword of love she carried, whose fiery blade, even when it appeared to strike at those it was defending, was only intent on cleaving a clear way to God, and thus fulfilment and happiness, through the morass of sin, human failings, obstacles, call them what you will, cluttering the approach between the spirit and its goal.

She was never absolutely certain, realizing that what appeared to her to be a fault might very well be, on account of the intention, an act of virtue. And although she might press to the point of unkindness, her vigorous actions, even at their most extreme, always halted this side of the line.

"We must not be *justices of peace*, but *angels of peace*," she was fond of saying, and then the angel would lay by her sword.

2

But let us lay by our pencils and pick up, for a moment, our more descriptive brushes.

Let it be a summer's afternoon. Let there be roses blooming.

Zinnias, their flat-colored discs balanced directly on top of their stems, seem to be sizzling in the heat. The honey-scented buddleia bush is sprinkled with little sulphur butterflies. Indeed, all the flower-beds are buzzing.

We glimpse them beyond the cloisters which are slotted with a ribbon of glancing gold.

Here she comes, the humble nun who yet moves with the gait of a princess. Twenty years old. . . .

There is a round white rose in the garden which seems to have been sculptured out of snow, and if snow had a fragrance its scent would be as sheer and pure and delicate as just such a flower. Her face is that rose, still retaining its stolid Normandy character, yet made translucent and chiselled by the breath of the Spirit and the discipline of the Rule.

As she glides, lit and unlit, past the ugly brick arches and columns, we are amazed at her beauty. The white coif seems to enhance her pallor rather than to detract from it. Oh, but it is dangerous surely to be as white as that! . . .

Past the plaster statue of the Child Jesus, before whom the close-packed bowl of purple sweet-peas she has placed there glimmers like a huge faceted amethyst, out into the chestnut walk she moves, past the Grotto of St. Mary Magdalen, past the blue-smocked gardener looking up from his rake and drawing back from the path as if he were afraid his honest dirt might sully her—she acknowledges his politeness by smiling at the ground—out, right out of the confines of the somber alley, into the lighter spaces of the orchards.

The snow of blossoms has dissolved now, and clusters of fruit, still green but swelling, are beginning to puff out the frills of the leaves.

The novices, their needles pricking and flashing when the sun catches them through the jagged holes in the foliage, are disposed in a half-circle under the boughs.

Good!—then we are to be allowed to remain out-of-doors. Mother Agnes, sensible woman, has granted her permission. Mother Marie Gonzague might not have done so, but who cares about her opinion today? Her authority is temporarily in abeyance, let her bite back her irritable assiduity for a month or two, it will do her no harm.

We are going to sit here under the apple-lit canopies, with the soothing vista of the long fields, their flat tranquillity shimmering a little in the heat, their sedate placidity disturbed occasionally by nothing more arbitrary than cropping cows.

We put the idea into Mother Agnes' head because we were feeling the strain of being shut up for so long ourselves, and did not wish to communicate it to the reader. It is so easy to become too serious, to allow religion to get on one's nerves. Sometimes, perhaps, Thérèse did not realize that. Her intenseness is often almost comic, but her own sense of humor usually steps in in time.

She is smiling at the moment as if she had a pleasurable secret to impart, a little surprise hidden away in those long baglike sleeves—and so she has, that is exactly where it is hidden. As she enters the circle, she takes it out and shakes it in the air and before her novices' round-eyed curiosity. What is it? A tube of marbled cardboard apparently, but it rattles. The ends are made of clear and ground glass respectively.

She applies the clear end to her eye, and twists the cylinder about.

"Oh!" she exclaims, "how lovely! Oh, but that is *beautiful!*"

The sisters wait. Their obedient silence is charming, but they cannot contain their bright inquisitiveness. It shines from their faces as if they were so many oval mirrors reflecting the sparkling light.

Little Mother Thérèse beckons her daughter, Sister Marie of the Trinity—who is actually eight years older than herself— and guides her to look through the tube.

What can it be? A telescope?

But no, Sister Marie does not see an enlarged bird or apple, but a magical design like a stained-glass window. But where has it come from?

Standing behind her, Thérèse gently twists the tube. Click! The design has changed to a jewelled honeycomb. Click! It is a pattern of overlapping multicolored stars.

Sister Marie emits little squeals of excitement and pleasure. The young nuns cannot remain composed a moment longer. They are all on their feet, eager for a turn.

The mysterious machine is passed from hand to hand, not without a considerable amount of reluctance on the part of the one who is looking, and much trembling impatience on the part of her who waits.

When they have all taken a peep, Thérèse sits and unscrews the instrument into her lap. She up-ends it, and a little collection of heterogeneous rubbish falls on the scoop of brown serge. Two or three bits of broken bottle glass, a few cheap beads, some snippets of black paper. . . . It is most disillusioning. Then she drops them back, adding a white-headed pin from somebody's workbasket and a daisy out of the grass. The tube is sealed, and everybody looks again. Again the gasps of wonder and delight. Then follows the lesson, the lesson of the kaleidoscope.

Thérèse claps her hands for attention.

The nuns settle, the air is quiet again, except for the birds who are under no compulsion to obey anybody. They are not in need of correction. Yet the blackbird does sound a little guilty, as he emits that odd, afternoon, fruit-stealing note, nothing like the full puissant whistle, but a dry self-conniving sort of sound, as if his tongue had become the wooden clapper of a rattle for scaring birds, but only half-swung in the hand of a boy nearly asleep in the heat. But our thoughts are straying . . . we must listen to her, not to the blackbird.

"So long as our actions, *even the very least*, remain within the *focus of love*," comes the voice—how quiet yet compelling it is. When she is teaching no one can refrain from attending, no one is bored. "Within the *focus of love*," she repeats, "then the Blessed Trinity, which is figured by the three converging mirrors in this toy, reflects them, and endows them with a wondrous beauty, so that Jesus finds our proceedings always pleasing to Him. But if we leave the ineffable center of Love, what will He see?" (Again she tips out the contents.) "Mere straws . . . actions sullied and nothing worth."

How unaffected, how charming, how easy to understand. She was never cryptic, except about herself.

She tried to console people, not so much by comforting words—her remarks although simple are often as cold-seeming and hard as stones—but by constant prayer and the offering of her daily pangs. It was as if she dare not trust her warm humanity, knowing it to be contaminated, preferring the purer way of assisting her clients from a distance—then her love stood a better chance of being more completely detached and disinterested.

When a novice came to her with some problem she tried not to let her alert interest in the psychological construction of beings take any pleasure, being very careful never to pursue, by questioning, some fascinating avenue opened up for a second by her suppliant, then closed by a sudden branching off, a nervous changing of the subject. She was not going to treat souls as a diversion.

She seemed to be very much against outward signs of emotion, encouraging the storing up of feeling. It seemed a dissipation to her when people complained or rhapsodized. If it were all kept inside, it became like an incandescence, a gas, and the soul would rise like the new balloon.

Although she had been a veritable cry baby herself (had she forgotten this? When someone who was at school with her was asked what she was like, their first reaction had been to remark: "Oh, she was a funny little thing—always crying.")—yes, although she had wept copiously in her early days, she was harshly against tears in others. Perhaps it was because of that. The "gift of tears" such as had been granted to St. Mary Magdalen, was a different matter—those copious sighs and drops were the winds of the Spirit, precious pearls—not fractiousness, not self-indulgence.

One told her she was going to confide and weep at Jesus' feet.

"Shed tears before the good God!" she exclaimed. "Take care you do no such thing. Far less before Him than before creatures ought you to exhibit signs of sadness. He has but our monasteries, this dear Master, to rejoice His heart; He comes to us to find a little repose, to forget the continual lamentations of His friends in the world, who, for the most part, instead of recognizing the value of the Cross, meet it with repining and tears; and would you behave like the generality of people? . . . Frankly, that is not disinterested love, it is *for us to console Jesus, not for Jesus to console us.* . . . He is, I know, so kind of heart that if you weep He will dry your tears, but afterwards He will go away sorrowful, not having been able to find in you the repose He sought."

Well, well, perhaps she was right, in a way, but such tense white indignation must have thrust to the heart of the unfortunate novice like the jet of a blow-lamp! Let us hope it burned up the dross quickly, and left the poor creature untrammelled, better equipped, once she had recovered from the shock, to go forward in peace.

Was this the same girl, one wonders, who had formed such a distressing habit of crying that Thérèse produced a scallop-shell, with the instruction that the moment she felt the drops likely to start, she was to place the sharp-edged object under her eyes and weep into that? Of course, in such ludicrous circumstances, the tears were stanched immediately!

But—and this is rather touching—when Thérèse was near her end, the same novice came to her bedside and asked permission to weep when she was dead. Really, the conditions of that nineteenth-century Carmel were often morbidly comic! Thérèse, glancing out of her agony with a look of mock-serious consideration, is said to have replied, eventually: "Yes—you may do so." Adding, with grim humor, as the novice turned contentedly away, "But only into the shell."

CHAPTER EIGHT

❧

Was She an Artist?

I

IN MOST CARMELITE convents the enclosure oratory backs directly on to the altar-wall of the church proper. This wall is pierced by a grated arch containing a "turn." For exposition of the Blessed Sacrament the priest from his side places the monstrance on the circular platform, twirling the contraption round until the Host is exposed in the chapel beyond.

Thérèse was suddenly commanded to cover the whole of this wall, on the nuns' side, with a mural. Prior to this her experience of painting had amounted to little more than devout pictures and illuminated texts on a quite small scale, so that this large work was, naturally, a considerable undertaking.

When she was a child and drawing lessons had been mooted, one of her older sisters had put in that Thérèse showed little aptitude for them and the project had been summarily dismissed, much to the latter's disappointment, for she had at the time felt a strong inclination to that subject, but in order to mortify herself had remained silent.

Those in authority must have known what they were about in ordering the wall-picture. Certainly Thérèse approached the task with her accustomed confident humility, which could so easily have been mistaken for complacence. She did not feel very capable, but no doubt the idea appealed to her greatly, and all she had to do was to be obedient, pray, and wield the brushes according to the scanty knowledge she had picked up in the course of the years. God would do the rest. It did not have to be perfect. And, indeed, it was not. An extremely devout contemporary prioress of another house has described it, not irreverently, as ghastly!

Without becoming a Carmelite of Lisieux it is practically impossible to see the actual work itself, but there is a difficult-to-come-by photographic reproduction. This prevents us from making any comment on the colors, but we may take it they were probably pretty and flower-like, for if the picture appears sentimental, which it undoubtedly does, it has also a quality of charm and lightness.

The center of the wall is taken up by the arch of the tabernacle. This forms the central point of the composition. The whole of the background is clouds. A kind of garland of angels' heads surrounds the arch. They are really the faces of little girls of the period, whose lace collars have become feathery wings. Some have dimpled arms, in the crooks of which are carried harps, wreaths, and sprays of field flowers, wheat, and berries; one swings a censer. A sleeping child, with a harp and marguerites, seeming to rest its head on a round-elbowed little arm supported by the arch itself, Thérèse admitted to be a representation of herself.

Beneath the garland of heads two more winged children, this time complete with torsos draped in garments like white nightdresses, their lower limbs fading away in their skirts and the clouds, carry between them a banner of ribbon on which is inscribed in simple capital lettering (it is gilt, we are told): SI VOUS CONNAISSIEZ LE DON DE DIEU! (If you knew what God has given us!)

The whole is a curious mixture of naïveté, painstaking execution, and, we were about to add, hackneyed inspiration, if such an expression were possible. But it is not entirely hackneyed. Its style is anything but original, being based on the typical bourgeois "taste" of the time, which one might see repeated again and again on first Communion cards, memorials to the deceased, parlor pictures of insipid piety, and yet there is just something in it of the appealing Teresian childlikeness.

Is it a work of art? The answer is no. It is no more a work
of art than any of the rest of her pictorial handicraft. But it
does show that she had a gift for drawing and painting which
might have been developed into an art, had she not been
hedged in by, had not submitted (for the purposes of mortification perhaps?) to the requirements of her environment. We
should be guilty of a too biased affection if we were to admit
to have discovered in it anything more promising than that.

So much for her painting.

2

Her writings are not so easy to assess.

Mr. Sacheverell Sitwell has said that in some of her simple
verses he has found signs of a truly poetic imagination. But
we will leave her poetry until the final section of this chapter.

Her letters we have already mentioned.

Is letter-writing an art? That it has had its exponents, perhaps still has, even in these days of hurried questions and
answers, cannot be denied, and as we shall see when we come
to examine certain of those she wrote to the Abbé Bellière—
and there are other excellent examples we shall have to admit that, despite the many instances of sentimentality and
absurdity, there were occasions when Thérèse succeeded in
composing epistles comparable to the finest letter-writers of
any age.

But the saint's chief literary output was her autobiography—
L'Histoire d'une Âme, or as it is titled in English, *Saint Thérèse
of Lisieux, The Little Flower of Jesus.*

Before we go on to examine this important work it will be
interesting to mention something of the circumstances in which
it was written.

One night in the winter of 1894 when the nuns were at
evening recreation, Thérèse was entertaining her two sisters,
Mother Agnes of Jesus and Sister Marie of the Sacred Heart,

with anecdotes of her childhood. She had always been adept at storytelling, and as a schoolgirl the tales she had recounted among her fellow pupils in the playground had succeeded also in drawing about her a circle of the older students. She had a way of describing situations and persons with such verisimilitude that her hearers were held by it.

It was the same on this occasion. With sudden illustrative gestures and subtle mimicry, expressed through the means of a quicksilver personality, she conjured up the scene and its protagonists like a brilliant impersonator in the theatre.

Probably for purely personal reasons—certainly she had no idea of the enormous significance of what she was proposing— Sister Marie suggested to Mother Agnes that she should get Thérèse to write an account of these things.

It is not customary for Carmelite nuns to write—prayer is their chief activity—although it may be argued that St. Teresa of Avila certainly proved the exception! Perhaps Mother Agnes had remembered this when she agreed to her sister's persuasions and gave the order to Thérèse to put her impressions on paper.

Thérèse herself was reluctant, as she thought it might distract her from more important matters, but of course she obeyed. We might mention here that towards the end when she insisted, as if under divine compulsion, that her autobiography should be published, she was at the same time firmly set against any other nun writing her reminiscences, and was definitely opposed to Carmelites conducting correspondence with outsiders, although she herself had been for the last two years of her life in continual communication with two missionaries. It hardly sounds fair, but what must be remembered is that she sought none of these privileges, accepting them as duties under obedience. If she had been commanded to burn her manuscripts she would have complied with the same alacrity.

Even so, as her book was about God's mercies she felt it incumbent upon her to advertise them.

"The manuscript must be published after my death without the slightest delay. If you put off doing it, if you are rash enough to speak to anyone, except to our mother, about it, the devil will lay countless snares to prevent the publication, and yet it is so important. But if you do all that lies in your power not to let it be hindered, do not fear any of the difficulties you will meet with. In the case of my mission, as in that of Joan of Arc, the will of God will be accomplished despite the envy of men."

"You think, then, that by means of this book you will do good to souls?" she was asked.

"Yes," she replied, "it is a means which God will employ."

A penny exercise book was obtained, and in her spare moments, which were few, she set about her composition without any preliminaries other than prayers to the Mother of God to guide her pen. She wrote in a clear upright classical hand, not, as some might have expected, with round romantic flourishes. It is not surprising she wrote unhesitantly, she did everything like that, and in any case what she was about now had been maturing in her mind for over twenty years.

In accordance with the instructions given her she handed the completed manuscript to Mother Agnes of Jesus on the evening of her feast day, the 21st January, 1896, as the latter was stepping into the choir. The nuns were in the middle of another election, and Mother Agnes was doubtless preoccupied. She placed the document in a drawer, and forgot all about it until two months later. Mother Marie Gonzague was re-elected Prioress on this occasion, and tidying up before reassuming the somewhat less responsible position of a simple nun, Sister Agnes, as she was called again now, came upon the manuscript and read it for the first time.

She was more than impressed. There was something here which should be given greater prominence, she was convinced of that, but she was no longer in authority to do anything about it herself.

The work only carried Thérèse's life to the point when she entered Carmel, there was nothing about her experiences as a *religieuse,* and it seemed very important to Sister Agnes that this lack should be remedied without delay.

The illness which was to draw Thérèse out of this world— how slowly and with what dreadful agony—had already made itself evident. There was no time to be lost. Sister Agnes prayed, took the simple blue exercise book (if it had been made of vellum and gold and studded with jewels it would not have been precious enough for its contents) to Mother Marie Gonzague, got her to read it, then kneeling implored her that she command her young dying sister to continue to write.

Mother Marie Gonzague, despite her rashness and irascibility, was no fool, had never been a fool as far as Thérèse was concerned, however unjustly she may have appeared to treat her, immediately affirmed.

So, wheeled out into the sunshine beyond the alley of her beloved *marroniers,* Thérèse, so enfeebled that she could no longer dip a pen into an ink-bottle, wrote in pencil the last account of her wonderful yet unremarkable life.

"We must economize," she said. "We must write between the lines."

"Oh no, dearest," replied Sister Agnes (in the circumstances she may be excused the too affectionate epithet), "you must not give yourself that trouble—not now."

But she did write between the lines, in another sense, as we shall see.

That was how it was constructed. There were no chapters. It was split up into that form later by Father Godfrey, a Premonstratensian, at the instigation of the Carmel.

Section One (the first eight chapters) she wrote for Mother Agnes; Section Two (chapters nine, ten, eleven and, twelve) she wrote for Mother Marie Gonzague; and the third and last Section (chapter thirteen), which was incorporated into the final version, she had written prior to chapters eight and nine, at the request of Sister Marie of the Sacred Heart, who had asked her for some consoling words to remember her by.

It will be seen by this that the work was not planned. Yet for a work of art a form is necessary. There is the feeling and there is the technique, and these attributes must be inextricably bound up in each other.

But there is more than one kind of artist. For instance, there are some who conceive an idea then carefully and calmly work it out, but in another category the creator appears so possessed by a vision that the shape of the work arises unselfconsciously. It is to the latter class that St. Thérèse belongs. The discipline of a Carmelite was enough to keep her demon in order.

Despite her logical systems, St. Teresa of Avila's works could hardly be described as methodical—they emerge with the designs of lumps of crystals. Her spiritual daughter has produced, as one might expect, something with the effect of a bush of roses. In both cases the form is organic. It seems to have grown as in nature. Works of this sort have a peculiar charm of their own, so that their deviations and imperfections are positive as one might refer to the irregularities of rocks or flowers.

Apart from its rambling, and the bright flash of gaiety which is concomitant with all the activities of Carmel, St. Thérèse's work cannot be likened further to that of her great mother. It is too indefinably original to be likened to anything but itself.

The style is rarely ornamental, though it is not without occasional sentimentalities and clichés which are burnt up, or absorbed, by the fire of its inspiration. It is almost always direct, and there are passages already quoted, *e.g.* her childhood vision of her father, her visit to the Pope, etc., which are expressed with a classical simplicity too deeply moving to be gainsaid.

It is, indeed, quite apart from the grace which informs it, the two opposite qualities of uncompromising uniformity and soaring romanticism, which often begin by confusing the reader, and at a first approach sometimes leave an unsatisfactory impression, that ultimately, if one is prepared to read the book again, result in a fusion and harmony which millions have found irresistible.

So this memorial of an obscure Carmelite nun, which was printed in the first place to be sent merely to the sister-houses of the order, continues to sell and sell, has travelled the length and breadth of the globe, and has been translated into almost as many languages as there are different peoples. This could not have happened if the book had not contained a universal message.

3

Finally, we come to her poems.

It has always been the custom of Carmelites to make a glad sound. Almost all Thérèse's verses were composed for that purpose. They were written to be sung, and—what we must not forget to take into account when we are criticizing them—the music was supplied first and the words had to be made to fit, a condition sufficiently awkward to cramp the style of the most accomplished.

Such was the naïveté and charming innocence of the Order that they often sang their hymns to tunes which, in the world, were coupled with words of a quite other significance. It mattered little to them what profane uses they had been put to previously, the gifted songstress in their midst would soon change all that.

Thus it will be seen that Thérèse came to write her poems under the burden of a considerable handicap. Did she find it irksome? Undoubtedly she must have done so. A spontaneity such as hers was not meant to be confined in such conventional birdcages. Discipline, yes, but not a conformation to an outworn mode, which in many instances was little better than a jingle. Still, she persisted, and from time to time her inspiration flashes and trills irresistibly from behind the wires of its gilded and over-decorated prison.

It would be out of place in a work such as we are undertaking here to go into a detailed analysis, so we will content ourselves with a brief generalization and a few typical illustrations of the best she has given us.

Everything is, of course, imbued with the spirit of the religious life. She sings all the time of the soul's ineffable yearning to be released from its place of exile and to be gathered up into the eternal brightness and happiness of the Homeland.

Her imagery is all of wings, stars, little boats, flames, flowers, and thirsts and dews. A great burning suspiration sighs through every line. She is always in a state of ecstasy; chaste, virginal, and rapt. But at the same time she is very objective, and her flights, however airy, take off from a solid scriptural foundation. It is this sound theological basis that her champions always refer to when her æsthetic merits are called into question. That it was a sufficient reason for her to write may be granted, but it has little to do with poetry as such.

You do not have to be a Christian to write a poem, and the fact that you are a Christian does not make you into a poet!

Indeed, it is possible to be a poet without writing any poetry at all, as in the case of Dorothy Wordsworth, for instance, who, in the pages of her journal, often showed as much, if not more, poetic sensibility than her celebrated brother.

But we are digressing. . . . Let us look at some of the poems of St. Thérèse. The translations are *not* poetry but merely literal versions of the French.

The trouble with her poems is they are all much too long. Twenty verses meant nothing to her. And this prevents our quoting even one of her words in its entirety.

"The Song of the Holy Face," as with several others, contains examples of emotional frankness such as one might find in poems addressed to an earthly lover. One is reminded of the Song of Solomon. For instance:

"Bientôt, de ta bouche adorée,
Donne-moi l'éternel baiser!"

"Soon, from your adorable mouth, give me that everlasting kiss!"

And again from the poem "Song of St. Agnes":

"De son sang précieux je suis tout empourprée.
Je crois goûter déjà les délices du ciel!
Et je puis recueillir sur sa bouche sacrée
Le lait avec le miel."

"I am clothed in the purple of His precious blood. Already I believe I taste the deliciousness of Heaven. But then I shall suck milk and honey from His holy mouth. . . ."

She had a great devotion to Joan of Arc, and all her poems on this theme are good. The following verse from "The Prayer of Joan of Arc in her Prison" has a gleam of real poetry:

"Je ne reverrai plus la montagne lointaine
Dont le sommet neigeux se plonge dans l'azur,
Et je n'entendrai plus, de la cloche incertaine,
Le son doux et rêveur onduler dans l'air pur."

"I shall see no more the far-off mountain, its snowy peak sprung into the blue, and no more will I hear the sweet chime of the hesitant clock, soft and dream-like, rippling the pure air."

The following simple lines from "What I Love" contain a similar moving romanticism:

"O souvenir! tu me reposes,
Tu me rappelles bien des choses . . .
Les repas du soir, le parfum des roses,
Les Buissonnets pleins de gaieté,
L'été."

"O memory! You fill me with peace, you remind me of so many things . . . our little suppers, the scent of the roses, Les Buissonnets full of gaiety, and the summer."

We could go on culling other like flowers from among the overgrown and sometimes weed-strangled beds of her garden,

but will conclude with a comment on a long and very delightful poem called "The Little Beggar of Christmastide." This is
typically Carmelite and Teresian. It was specially composed
for the convent festivities of Christmas 1885, and is really a
sort of poetic charade.

An angel (was this Thérèse herself, one wonders?) appears
carrying in her arms the Child Jesus. She sings of the mystery
of the Incarnation, then, having placed the Holy Child in the
manger, presents to the Mother Prioress, and then to each
Carmelite, a basket filled with "billets," each sister draws one,
and without opening it gives it to the angel, who sings the alms
asked for by the Divine Infant.

There are twenty-six little notes altogether, which means
there must have been (including, of course, the aged) twenty-
seven nuns in the Carmel at that time.

Here is a list of what Jesus requests, each object symbolic of
some aspect of charity, which is explained by the angel:

A Golden Throne	A Flower
Some Milk	Some Bread
Little Birds	A Mirror
A Star	A Palace
A Lyre	A Crown of Lilies
Roses	Bonbons
A Valley	A Caress
The Reapers	A Cradle
A Bunch of Grapes	Diapers
A Little Host	Fire
A Smile	A Cake
A Toy	Some Honey
A Pillow	A Lamb

Each object is expressed in terms of the most delicate purity.
We will quote from three of them:

Des Roses
"*. . . Ah! si je chéris la blancheur*
Des lis, symboles d'innocence,
J'aime aussi la riche couleur
Des roses de la pénitence."

Roses
". . . Oh—although the whiteness of the lily, the symbol of innocence, is most dear to me, I love also the blushes of the penitent rose . . ."

Des Bonbons
"*. . . Les pralines du Carmel*
Qui charment le Roi du ciel,
Ce sont tous vos sacrifices.
Ma sœur, votre austérité,
Votre grande pauvreté,
De Jésus font les délices!"

Sweets
". . . The King of Heaven likes toffees from Carmel, and they consist of all your little sacrifices—your asceticism, my sister, and your poverty, these make delicious sweets of Jesus!"

Un Berceau
"*. . . Si vous saviez le plaisir*
Que l'enfant trouve à dormir
Sans crainte qu'on réveille,
Vous serviriez de berceau
A Jésus, le doux Agneau
Souriant lorsqu'il sommeille."

A Cradle
"If you only knew how nice it is for the baby Jesus when he is not woken up frightened, you yourselves would want to be His cradle—the little lamb who smiles for you in His sleep."

Well, was St. Thérèse an artist? What do you think? Father Petitot says:

"Between an artist and a saint there is this difference, that the artist makes the execution of some work outside himself his end in life, whereas a saint pursues only one aim, his own sanctification, the perfecting of his own life. . . ."

But sanctity is a potential for all of us, just as we are. One could be both.

※

CHAPTER NINE

The Dart of Fire

I

AFTER WHAT MUST have seemed an eternity of being buried alive—for years now the alert soldier's body had been little more than a coffin of flesh—Monsieur Martin's spirit departed this life, and it could be inscribed on an official certificate that he was legally dead.

Naturally the loss of a father as loved as he was must have proved a crisis of ineffable sorrow to his children, but one may imagine their tears were also expressive of a deep-felt relief that the cruelty of his sufferings had abated at last.

Thérèse was convinced he had gone straight to heaven, but for once she asked God for a sign.

Céline, free now to join her sisters in religion, was meeting with formidable opposition from, strangely enough, that very quarter where she might most have expected encouragement, the Carmel itself. Certain members of the community were afraid the admittance of yet another Martin would give them undue prominence, making a clique, as it were, and the fostering of a too natural family feeling amongst those who had committed themselves to spiritual sisterhood only.

Eventually all but one had been persuaded that Céline, who had endured her baptism of fire in the world so courageously and uncomplainingly, would be an asset to the convent rather than a liability; but as it was apparently necessary for the community to be unanimous on this point, the deadlock remained.

It was over this matter that Thérèse asked for the sign.

"If my father has escaped the fires of purgatory, and been

received immediately into bliss," she prayed, "let me know this by the removal of all objections to Céline's entrance here."

She had hardly risen from her knees before the nun in question came to her and told her she had changed her mind, and that it now seemed to her essential for the good of the Order that Céline should be received into it.

So that was that. Monsieur Martin was in paradise, and a few weeks later Céline was in the garden of Carmel. The date was the 14th September, 1894. This reunion with the "twin bantam" or "double daisy" was undoubtedly, whatever its higher significance, a rare taste of human earthly happiness for Thérèse.

Of course she tried to mortify it! After the conventional embrace when Céline passed through the enclosure door, Thérèse turned away, but Mother Marie Gonzague, with one of those sympathetic touches her detractors have been at too much effort to deny, called her back, commanding her with an acerbity which concealed her own deep feelings to conduct her newly arrived sister to her allotted cell.

So another year passed under the sweet monotony of the rule—sweet when it was not bitter.

They were all "home" now. Léonie too seemed to have found a nest, having returned to the Visitation Convent at Caen. Alas, her vocation was still premature, and she had to be thrust out weeping bitterly—just how bitterly only God knew—into the world again. Monsieur and Madame Guérin, about to part with their daughter Marie, who was to join her cousins in the Carmel next year, found a place on their own hearth for this queer, embarrassingly disconsolate relation. But she would not stay there for ever. After four years the call would come again, and this time its promises would be fulfilled.

Thérèse, her dryness hidden away more secretly than an instrument of penance—indeed, it was as if the barbed cross of her early days in the convent now hung inside her, knocking against her very heart—went about her tasks with the unnoticeable regularity of a growing flower. Yes, the spiritual flower was beginning to unfold to full bloom at the cost of the flower of her flesh, which was already, at the age of twenty-two years, on the brink of decline.

It was the price exacted by unmitigated mental and physical toil. She had been pruning herself of every superfluity almost since the beginning of her will, and indirectly that relentless uncompromising force was having its effect on a constitution always refined and delicate, undermined now by the physical rigors it had endured in the ascent of Carmel.

The luminous whiteness of her complexion, the loose bronchial cough which had of late become small and hard and persistent, a certain dilated glitter in the eyeballs, all these were signs which, for the purposes of the inexplicable Will of God, were seemingly to be ignored by her fellows, or at any rate, at this stage, nothing was to be done about them. Eventually every primitive means available would be resorted to, by which time it would be too late.

She herself was only concerned that she should not fail in her religious duties, and not inconvenience her sisters by, for instance, keeping them awake at night by that exasperating dry hacking, as if someone were tapping at the hollow of her throat with a chisel.

Her quick changes of color—the result, no doubt, of fever—played curious tricks on the community's powers of observation.

She entered the parlor. A nun working there looked up and was evidently so shocked by the saint's haggardness that she broke silence.

"Oh, sister!" came the horrified exclamation, "you look so ill—I fear you will not be able to continue with us."

Thérèse passed from the parlor to the cloister. A lay sister was sweeping up the dead rose leaves before the statue of the Infant Jesus. She was a simple soul, somewhat inclined to be garrulous perhaps.

"Sister Thérèse," she murmured admiringly, "I must tell you, you are looking so well today—positively radiant!"

From that time forth Thérèse was no longer concerned for the opinions of creatures. She knew, anyway, she was all imperfect. God saw her as she really was, and loved her. What did it matter how she appeared in the eyes of others?

But all most be made positive. If, in any case, she was going to be ill, it must be turned into love, like everything else.

It was at about this time that she received the grace to offer herself as a victim. That last formal relinquishment of her human rights, the final and ultimate abandonment of herself into the everlasting arms of Love.

She has recorded it thus:

"While thinking one day of those who offer themselves as victims to the Justice of God, and who turn aside the punishment due to sinners, taking it upon themselves, I felt such an offering to be both noble and generous. I was very far, nevertheless, from feeling myself drawn to make it, and from the depths of my heart I cried: 'O my Divine Master, shall Thy Justice alone find atoning victims? Has not *Thy Merciful Love* need of them also? On every side it is ignored and rejected . . . those hearts on which Thou wouldst lavish it turn to creatures and seek their happiness in the miserable satisfactions of a moment, rather than cast themselves into Thy arms—into the ecstatic fires of Thy infinite Love O my God, must that Love which is disdained lie hidden in Thy Heart? It seems to me that if Thou shouldst find souls offering themselves as a holocaust to Thy Love, Thou wouldst consume them rapidly and wouldst be pleased to set free those flames of infinite tenderness now imprisoned in Thy Heart. If Thy Justice which avenges itself upon earth must needs be satisfied, how much more must Thy Merciful Love desire to inflame souls, since "Thy Mercy reacheth even to the Heavens"! O Jesus, permit that I may be that happy victim—consume Thy holocaust with the fire of Divine Love'."

Of course, before committing herself she had to obtain the permission of her superiors, and then a document was drawn up—one could hardly call it a contract, for she made no claims on the Other Party other than that He should take possession of her soul. She petitioned for His Love. The paper was placed in her little book of the Gospels and was to be carried in her bosom until the hour of her death.

It read as follows:

✠

J. M. J. T.
An offering of myself
as a burnt-offering
To the Merciful Love of the
Good God.

"O my God! Blessed Trinity, I desire to *love* You and make You *loved*, to work for the glorification of Holy Church by saving souls on earth and delivering souls in Purgatory. I desire to accomplish Your Will perfectly and attain the degree of glory You have prepared for me in Your Kingdom. In a word, I desire to be a saint, but I feel my powerlessness, and I ask You, O my God, to be Yourself my Sanctity. Since You have so loved me as to give Your only Son to be my Saviour and my Spouse, the infinite treasures of His merits are mine, I offer them to You with joy, begging You to look at me only with the Face of Jesus between, and in His Heart burning with *Love*.

"I offer You too all the merits of the Saints, in Heaven and on earth, their acts of *Love* and those of the Holy Angels; finally I offer You, *O Blessed Trinity*, the *Love* and the merits of the *Blessed Virgin, my dearest Mother*, to her I yield up my offering, asking her to present it to You. Her divine Son my *Beloved* Spouse, said to us in the days of His mortal life: 'Whatsoever you shall ask My Father in My Name, He will give it to you!' So I am certain that You will grant my desires.

O my God! I know that 'the more You mean to give, the more You make us want'. In my heart I feel immeasurable desires, and it is with confidence that I ask you to come and take possession of my soul. Ah! I cannot receive Holy Communion as often as I desire, but, Lord, are you not all-powerful? Remain in me, as in the tabernacle, never leave Your little victim. . . .

"I want to console You for the ingratitude of the wicked, and I beg You to take away my freedom to displease You, and if at times I fall through weakness, I beg that Your *divine gaze* may purify my soul instantly, consuming all my imperfections, as fire transforms everything into itself. . . .

"I thank You, O my God! for all the graces You have granted me, in particular for having made me pass through the crucible of suffering. It is with joy that I shall look upon You on the Last Day, bearing the scepter of the Cross; since You have deigned to give me that most precious *Cross* as my portion, I hope to be like You in Heaven, and see the sacred stigmata of Your Passion shining in my body.

"After earth's exile, I hope that I shall enjoy You in the Homeland, but my wish is not to amass merits for Heaven, but to work *solely for love* of You, with the single aim of giving You pleasure, consoling Your Sacred Heart and saving souls which will love you everlastingly.

"In the evening of this life I shall appear before You empty-handed, for I do not ask You, Lord, to count my works. All our justices have stains in Your sight. So I want to be clad in Your own Justice, and receive from Your *Love* the possession of *Your-self*. I want no other *Throne* or other *Crown* than *You*, O my *Beloved*! . . .

"In Your sight, time is nothing. A single day is as a thousand years, so that in an instant You can prepare me to appear before You.

"To live in an *act of perfect Love,* I OFFER MYSELF AS A BURNT OFFERING TO YOUR MERCIFUL LOVE, calling upon You to consume me at every instant, while You let the floods of *infinite tenderness* pent up within You flow into my soul, so that I may become Martyr to Your *Love*, O my God! . . .

"When that martyrdom has prepared me to appear before You, may it cause me to die, and may my soul hurl itself in that instant into the eternal embrace of *Your Merciful Love*. . . .

"At every heartbeat, O my *Beloved*, I wash to renew this offering an infinite number of times, till the shadows retire and I can tell You my Love over again, looking upon You face to face eternally.

Marie Françoise Thérèse of the Child Jesus
and of the Holy Face, rel. carm. ind.

Feast of the Most Holy Trinity,
9th June in the year of grace 1895."

2

Her offering was accepted.

A few days after having made her oblation she was in the choir about to begin the Stations of the Cross when there took place an extraordinary manifestation of God's love. She suddenly felt herself wounded by a dart of fire so ardent that she thought she should die. It was a kind of spiritual orgasm. Her seraphic mother, St. Teresa of Avila, had experienced it before her. In her case she had actually seen an angel carrying a long spear of gold the tip of which he had thrust several times into her heart, imbuing her with an ineffable ecstasy. After her death, when her incorrupt body was exhumed, and the heart exposed, it was seen to be scarred as with a wound of fire.

But there was to be no physical proof in the case of her young daughter. The latter's heart was to crumble into dust in accordance with her desire to be nothing. She admitted, when questioned by the Prioress, that she had experienced transports before, but not anything as overwhelmingly intense as this.

"It seemed," she said, "as though an invisible force plunged me wholly into fire. . . . But what fire! what sweetness!"

Another second and her soul would have departed her body. But the dart was withdrawn, and she sank back immediately into her habitual condition of aridity.

But it was enough. Her marriage with God had been consummated, and from now on she was to bring forth a family of all the virtues, although their birth would be accompanied by every conceivable pain, both of the body and of the soul.

CHAPTER TEN

꧙

The Divine Intimation

*"O my people what have I done to thee? or in what have
I afflicted thee?*
Answer me.
*Because I led thee out of the land of Egypt, thou hast
prepared a cross for thy Saviour.*
Holy God.
Holy God.
Holy strong one.
Holy strong one.
Holy immortal one, have mercy upon us.
Holy immortal one, have mercy upon us.

IT IS LENT, 1896, but soon the added austerities will be over,
and Christ will have risen again like the spring sunshine,
which is even now beginning to touch the dark places of the
shrouded Carmel with little flickers of gold—there, then gone
again, seeming hopeful premonitions of the great flood of
glory that will come to the now darkened earth on Easter Day,
actually in forty-eight hours.

But today is somber, and solemn, and terrible—the Black
Friday of the Crucifixion—Good Friday only in so far as it
is God who is good. This day little man has doused the Light
of the World, has been permitted to do so—what bitter irony!
—to conform to the Omnipotent Will for his ultimate salva-
tion.

It is awful in Carmel today, awful yet beautiful in a way
one falters in the attempt to describe.

Everything is dark, even the silence. The statues are masked
with depressing purple, not the King's purple, but a dead
miserable color that cannot glow. The nuns are like bent pyres
of blackened ash. It is the world's darkness that has descended

upon them, as when the rocks shuddered on the place of the skull, and the sun had become a hideous wen of blood skeined with hysterical rushing miasmas. Yet the little fingers of gold come and go, touching the congealed shadows. . . .

Thérèse prays with an extraordinary expression. Her face shines like a moon through her veil. She is identified with the Passion of her Lord, but an unearthly secret joy—yes, joy!— glitters from her as if it were tangible. In the early hours of this morning she received a message, a private message which she has committed to one other person only, the Mother Prioress. She had to do so according to obedience, as the message was very curious, and its implications, in the earthly sense, required prudent handling. But Mother Marie Gonzague, having listened, has not seen fit to make any alterations in the rule. Although the divine intimation has been—could have been—frightening, she has seen no reason why the day's harsh penances should be mitigated in the case of this her most strangely privileged daughter; though, prior to the message, she had forbidden Thérèse to watch all night with the rest of the community before the Altar of Repose. It had seemed to her then, apparently, that her daughter, whose frailty of body had been making itself more and more evident in the last months, would do better to go to bed rather than submit herself to the added fatigues of the long cold vigil.

Yet now, in spite of what Thérèse had told her, it appeared proper to her that her child should suffer something more. Why? Knowing the facts, most kind and sensible people would have excused the young nun every trial of the day, would have hastily piled on creature comforts, but not so that baffling mentor Mother Marie Gonzague. Why? Because she was, consciously or otherwise, fulfilling the Will of God. There could be no other reason for such, in the eyes of the world, fantastic behavior.

There has been the Mass of the Presanctified. This is the

one day of the year when God abstains from coming down to the altars of men.

The sisters have touched their cold lips with bread and water merely.

Now they are reverencing the Cross. A crucifix, its ivory figure suggestive of Christ's bones, has been placed on the chilly flags of the chapel, and each nun has prostrated herself and kissed the stretched nailed limbs.

Thérèse knows, despite the awful depression of the hour, the seeming eternal hour of God's death, when there is nothing left to mankind but despair, that the whole world with its terrible weight of materialism, its shrieking wounds—for the laughter of the pleasure-loving has become an agonized cry— and its stench of putrefaction that no perfume or deodorant can cover, she knows that this great ball of rags and filth, this ruin of Eden, could be rolled away and hidden for ever, dissolved in the hole on Christ's foot, for in proportion to Him it is no more than a speck, a granule of dust merely, no, less than that even, less than anything visible.

It is so wonderful, God's omnipotence and Love—if only people could understand. . . .

She prays herself into His Heart, prays to draw all mankind after her there, to the source and sea of all bliss. . . .

At last the day of sorrows is over, and the nuns, exhausted and stupefied by an empathy that has both nailed them to the gallows-tree and bowed them to the riven earth with the great archetypes of all the mourners, Mary, the mother, Mary, the lover, and John, the friend, have moved, they know not how, back to their cells, where they will remain buried with Christ in the tomb until the hour of awakening and resurrection.

Thérèse, breathing with the deep regularity of one in a trance, slowly—so slowly, because even the effort of raising her arms to unpin her coif is as if she were lifting a weight of iron—discards her coarse habit, but, still retaining the belt of prickly horse-hair, the ever desired embrace of pain, draws

on her nightrobe, stops the light of her (our) little lamp—
it is broken, the wick has always to be raised with a pin, she
chose it for that—and composes herself under the thin blanket.

She lies on her back, her arms crossed on her breast, and
stares up into the darkness.

So quiet . . . a mouse scrabbles and squeaks in the wall—
eventually no sound but the drum of her heart.

She waits, smiling.

Then, suddenly, as it had happened on the previous night,
it comes again.

A hot stream, sweet and sticky on her tongue, bubbles up
against her teeth.

As she had done last night, she takes her (our) handkerchief then, not looking, as before, pushes it away under the
straw pillow.

When the morning comes, when it is light again, she wakes
with the excited feeling of anticipatory happiness like a child
on Christmas Day.

She draws out the rag, and now looks at it fully.

Her face glows and opens like a white flower, a white rose
or a lily, under the beams of the sun.

The message is the same as yesterday.

It is written in red.

The sense is: "Your place is prepared for you. I am coming
to fetch you—soon, very soon. . . ."

It is a love-letter.

She closes her eyes for a second the better to savor the joy
of it.

Then the bell rings, and she jumps up.

PART THREE

The Gates of Heaven

The Two Worlds

Chevaux de Bois

"Tournez tournez; bons chevaux de bois,
tournez cent tours, tournez mille tours,
tournez souvent et tournez toujours,
tournez, tournez au son des hautbois . . ."

VERLAINE

I

IT HAS BEEN said the world is always with us, and in the sense of time it is true. As long as time lasts—no longer than that—there will be the world. The world is always the same; it adopts the fashions of its age, sometimes it is their creator, if to cast shadows may be said to be creative, for that is all the world can do. But it is only love which is truly creative, so we would be wrong ultimately in using that word in connection with the world.

The world out of its terrible ennui spins only illusions. Sometimes the illusions seem so real, for there is no clear dividing line between reality and unreality. The negatives and positives mingle, and it is only an act of love which can separate them. To look on events other than through the eyes of love is to see them only as a tangle.

It is how we see things most of the time: the wars, the millinery, the check books, the false treaties, the glittering, fascinating, alternately exciting and depressing surrealist jumble which appears to be life, and which only perhaps the artists and the saints can succeed in resolving so that in glimpses it becomes recognizable and meaningful.

Sustained sanctity sees it whole. That is why it is so re-assuring to look at it from behind the shoulders of the saints.

But we will look at it now, for a moment, through error and frailty, our common human eyes.

It is the world she would have looked out upon, though she would have seen it differently from us, had she not been immured behind the black curtain of Carmel.

2

1897. The nineteenth century is drawing to a close.

The previous tone, the quintessence of bourgeoisism, set by the great bourgeois leader Monsieur Thiers, still prevails, but among the intellectuals a spirit of criticism is beginning to assert itself, exemplified in the writings of Sainte-Beuve, Anatole France, and the agnostic Monsieur Renan.

"There may be more saints canonized by the Church," says the latter, "but no more will be canonized by the people." He will be proved wrong on that point in the comparatively short space of less than thirty years. Indeed the acclamations will begin before the century is out.

Naturalism, or realism, is coming into vogue. Flaubert's *Madame Bovary*, for example, and the enormous saga of the times by Zola, *Les Rougon-Macquart*, the natural and social history of a family of the period.

The Impressionist painters, Manet, Monet, Renoir, Dégas, led by their old father, Pissarro, are painting in terms of light, and thus metamorphizing ugliness into beauty.

Thérèse is in that movement too. The light she threw on middle-class tastelessness has made it gleam, so that the little parlor virtues have been exalted on to heroic pedestals. These highlights predominate, the pettiness and narrowmindedness are dissolved in the texture of the shadows. The hideous *immortelles* have been given a petal-delicacy and a perfume, are breathing as flowers alive. But it is not so noticeable yet. . . .

Compromise, respectability, hypocrisy, the keeping up of appearances, are still the tenets of the people's faith. The Church is a party to it too, as we shall see in a minute.

And of course excessive respectability has bred scandal. The exposure of the Panama Canal project, for instance, the injustice meted out to Captain Dreyfus. . . .

Pope Leo XIII is a clever man. He knows how to dangle the ball of the world as if the devil were no more malignant than a kitten. It is a question of expediency, that useful if uninspiring resource of statesmanship. Yes, this Pope, although still the Holy Father, is, as well as being a poet, also something of a politician.

The Third Republic had become identified in the minds of its friends and foes alike with hostility to the Church. But it was there to stay. The restoration of the monarchy, whose adherents were conservative and catholic, was a lost cause. Leo XIII had the worldly wisdom to realize it. If the Church's expectations were to be other than persecution, there was only one thing to be done, and that was to come to terms with the enemy.

The chosen spokesman was the popular Archbishop of Algiers and Carthage, Cardinal Lavigerie. He was instructed to instigate the policy of *Ralliement*. It was announced to the hierarchy that they were to prefer a Republican candidate if he gave adequate guarantee of religious freedom. Then Leo issued an encyclical, *Inter Multiplices Sollicitudines*, to bear it out.

Thus, to preserve his identity without interference, which, unmitigated by its recipient's clever concessions, might have eventually destroyed him, the Christian made friends for himself in the houses of Mammon. Priests accepted the new ruling of military service, and *le curé sac au dos* bore the weight of his pack humbly for the gratification of the extreme Left, and his own right to exist.

The poet Verlaine's wooden horses, the world's effigies,

glamorous, nostalgic, fierce-eyed yet sad, continued to turn in the Luxemburg Gardens. The new motors, their occupants goggled and dust-coated over bird-like elegance—ospreys were becoming increasingly fashionable among the ladies—jerked recklessly along the Champs Elysées at an excessive thirty miles an hour. The mirrors *chez* Maxims reflected the naked breasts and shoulders of the fabulous *demi-mondaines,* rising from their scented nests of jewels and flowers. Sarah Bernhardt, Réjane, Cécile Sorel, the priestesses of Melpomone, inducted the worshippers in the temples of the theatres. Sallow-faced ballet-girls, women ironing or imbibing absinthe were a kind of idealized mediocrity. Society found it *chic* to dip in squalor; the poets wore lice for buttonholes; genius and venereal disease were intimate playmates, and to be depraved, which was the mode—or rather the thing to read about—one had first to be smug and black-coated, otherwise there would be no thrill.

Thus the *petit rentier* class predominated, as did the little, the more insidious kinds of vice. Dust of lime-flowers fell between the fishing-rods projecting from the banks of the Seine . . . dust of lime-flowers and the dust of the world. The Kaiser glowered on the German border, but no more fighting yet, except for domestic squabbles.

The *carousel* turns, turns, the lime-flowers turn and fall down into the slow water, on to the sandal-trodden pathways of the garden of Carmel.

3

She has left her cell now, and is living, or dying, rather, in the infirmary. But it will take a long time. . . .

This afternoon they have pushed the ugly iron truckle bed out into the brick porch so that Sister Agnes can take a photograph, perhaps the last.

She is half sitting up, an uncomfortable posture, perhaps it is to protect her back, for her desire to become a holocaust is being fulfilled almost literally. Doctor La Néele has had recourse to an old-fashioned remedy to burn out the disease, and has cauterized her spine in over two hundred places.

It is tuberculosis, of course, and has been so neglected (probably greatly her own fault) as to have spread from the lungs to nearly every part of her anatomy. Heaven alone knows what the recently started organization for the treatment of this scourge, *L'Œuvre de la Tuberculose,* would have to say about the inadequate nursing facilities of the Carmel. In any case so little is known about it as compared to the present day. It was only in 1882 that Doctor Robert Koch succeeded in isolating the bacillus.

She has all the usual distressing symptoms, malaise, headache, thirst, sleeplessness, night-sweats, loss of appetite, vomiting, a great weight in the abdomen, accompanied by spasmic stabs, raying through her whole being like a terrible star of pain.

She is not beautiful today. Her skin is pale, sallow, and dry, puffy round the eyes, the expression of the mask drawn in, as is common to all those with deranged digestive organs. But it is going to get worse. Her bowels are going to be infected with gangrene, so that she will be able to say with the Psalmist: "I am a worm, and not a man," but she will also say with the prophet Job: "Even though He slay me, yet will I love Him."

Even so her obligatory smile for the picture is extraordinary. It is uplifting, but it is also terrible.

Despite the oppression to her breathing, she is still wearing her constricting nun's headgear. She carries her crucifix on her lap, and is at the strange occupation of wiping Christ's wounds with the petals of a deflowered rose. As they carry her indoors, she will call to the novice instructed to tidy the porch:

"Do not lose any of those. They will be useful later on."

Dead rose-leaves useful. What does she mean?

They have dragged creeper off the wall of the house, and

arranged it over the foot of the bed, to give, in their eyes, a charming effect to the photograph.

Sister Agnes takes some time setting up her tripod. The community dart about, patting pillows, smoothing out unbecoming wrinkles in the counterpane, the fall of leaves is not quite right—so! . . .

All this fuss is so exasperating, so ridiculous, but it must be borne along with her major trials, not least of which— it is perhaps more near unendurable than her physical torments —is her sudden lack of faith.

"If one judged by the poems I have composed this year," she said, "it might seem that I have been inundated with consolation, that I am a child for whom the veil of Faith is almost rent asunder. . . . But it is not a veil . . . it is a wall which reaches to the very heavens, shutting out the starry sky."

On the natural plane she is almost without a belief in God. Her involuntary thoughts are blasphemous. She is living in that black hole down there in the shrubbery. It is an apt allusion. There can be something terribly depressing about laurel walks. Who has not felt the utter emptiness, an emptiness peopled only by the fiends of Abaddon, a great gap, as it were, opening on to stark nothingness, when looking into the dank greenness of such places? . . . a green not of life and spring, but that decomposing green, that horrible sickly radiation, if it could be termed such, which illumines the lost places of the netherworld. The shade in its depths and about its roots is hell's shade, and she felt herself lying there, lost for eternity.

One night a voice hissed in her ear like a serpent:

"You dream of a land of light and fragrance, you believe that the Creator of these wonders will be for ever yours, you think to escape one day from the mists in which you now languish. Hope on! . . . Hope on! . . . Look forward to death! It will give you, not what you hope for, but a night darker still, the night of utter nothingness!"

Faithless, she has made innumerable acts of faith. The merits must be pure gold, but she feels, sees, nothing of them. Her belief is now, if that were possible, grounded on despair. Wonderful, but on the plane on which we live, what insupportable agony. She continues to compose her songs of joy, admitting that their rapturous contents are only what she wishes to believe. Humanly, she believes nothing, is entirely deserted. And by some strange freakish irony, another trick of the devil, many of the nuns think there is nothing wrong with her, that her illness is a sort of affectation, even the retching up of pieces of herself an affectation!

It is the dereliction of God on the cross she is experiencing, or at least something which makes us nearer to understanding it. She holds to that idea, so that it becomes a kind of miracle, changing the terrifying abysmal negation to one small positive flame glimmering in the thick blackness of the end of all things. Her night-sweats are as His holy sweats in the garden of agony. The mystery is she does not exude dew of blood as He did.

Sometimes she can do nothing but groan, then chooses silence, actually exercises choice with the last movements of consciousness. It is an indescribable martyrdom.

To help retain an expression of cheerfulness she goes over the dream she had last night.

It had done something, momentarily, to restore her belief in Heaven, as if in the midst of the tempest Jesus had commanded "the winds and the storm, and there was a great calm." But chaos set up its roaring again almost immediately.

She describes the dream thus:

". . . I found myself, during my sleep, in a gallery where I was walking alone with our Mother. On a sudden, without knowing how they had entered, I perceived three Carmelites clothed in their mantles and large veils, and I knew that they had come from heaven. Oh, I thought, how happy I should be if I could see the face of one of these Carmelites. As if my prayer had been heard, the tallest of the Saints came towards me and I fell on my knees. O Joy, she raised her veil, or rather held it up and covered me with it. Without any hesitation, I recognized the venerable Mother Anne of Jesus, foundress of the Carmel in France. Her countenance was beautiful, but of an unearthly beauty; no ray escaped from it, and yet, in spite of the thick veil which covered us both, I could see this celestial face illumined with an inffably soft light which seemed to be produced from it. The Saint loaded me with caresses, and seeing myself so tenderly loved, I made bold to say these words, 'O my Mother, I implore you to tell me if the good God will leave me long upon this earth? Will He come soon for me?' She smiled with tenderness, 'Yes, soon . . . soon, I promise you.' 'My Mother,' I continued, 'tell me also, does not the good God want something more of me than my poor little acts and my desires . . . is He satisfied with me?' Then the face of the venerable Mother shone with a new brightness, and her look appeared to me incomparably more tender. 'The good God wants nothing more of you,' she said to me. 'He is pleased, well pleased.' . . . And taking my head in her hands, she covered me with such caresses that it would be impossible for me to express the sweetness of them. My heart was overflowing with happiness, but I remembered my sisters and I wanted to ask some favors for them . . . alas, I awoke. . . ."

At last everything was ready for the picture, except that the sun had gone in.

She longs to shift her aching body, but refrains. Her cheeks ache with smiling. She offers it up. . . .

Eventually the grey valley clouds part, and an angel's finger irradiates the figure in the bed. Sister Agnes is about to press the shutter, when old Sister St. Pierre suddenly clatters her stick. By the time it is retrieved the sky has congealed.

They have to wait again.

CHAPTER TWO

✠

The Two Brothers

I

IF THÉRÈSE HAD been born a man she would probably have become a missionary.

Indeed, there was a time when she nearly did enter the mission field. Her transference to the Carmel at Hanoi was under consideration, and it had been almost decided that she should be sent there when the sudden breakdown in her health made it impossible. She would have liked to go, to make the sacrifice of leaving her natural sisters, as well as the other members of the convent family at Lisieux, and lose herself afresh in a company of strangers, but this painful satisfaction was to be denied her.

As if by way of consolation, though it had not been permitted for that purpose, she was suddenly allowed—commanded, one should say, for her own wishes were not consulted—to enter into a correspondence with two missionary priests, Père Roulland and the Abbé Bellière.

The latter did not reach full priesthood until after her death, when he became a member of the Order of the White Fathers.

Prior to this real contact with actual living men who had so thrillingly dedicated their lives to carrying the shining light of the Host into the dark and dangerous places of the East, Thérèse had offered a considerable amount of her love and prayer and sacrifice for missionaries, without knowing any by name. And she would do so until the end of her days.

When she was seen dragging herself slowly along the paths of the garden, and was asked why she exerted herself in this unnecessary way, when she had only to ring her bell and summon someone to push her wheelchair, she replied she was doing it to relieve the exhaustion of those travelling long foreign roads to deliver the Viaticum. And when, as a last resort, the most expensive drugs and tonics were provided in the hope of restoring a little of her dynamic energy which was (oh, so rapidly now!—yet agonizingly slowly under endurance) seeping out through the holes of her wrecked body, she prayed that their effects would, instead of benefiting herself, go to bring health to priests who were daily losing it in the cause of sowing the seed of Christ in the malarial paddy fields of China.

The letters began in June 1896.

The apostolate of the Abbé Bellière had been placed in her keeping in 1895, but the zeal with which she had undertaken his cause did not meet with any visible response—apart from a card to say he was going into barracks to begin his military service—until a year later. A delay of that sort was, of course, nothing new. Its only effect was probably that of causing her to redouble her prayers.

Père Roulland, when applying to the Carmel for a sister to aid him on the eve of his setting out for Su Chuen, was informed by Mother Marie Gonzague that in selecting Thérèse she had given him of all her good ones the best. Later this priest was called as a witness at the Process of Canonization. He died in 1934, while holding the office of Chaplain at the Convent of La Reconnaissance at Dorman, having, through modesty, refused a bishopric for which he had been chosen unanimously by the voters of the Society of Foreign Missions in 1917.

The Abbé Bellière was still a student when he made his request. Thérèse sustained him with letters and prayers for two years. He left to take up his duties with the White Fathers in Algiers the day before her death. After several years as a missionary in Africa he contracted sleeping sickness, returning to France to make his end in the home of his family at Lang-runes (Calvados) in 1907, aged thirty-three.

Something suggests that he was perhaps her favorite, but she showed no favoritism. Her words to them both reveal an exquisitely tactful sympathy such as one might almost expect from the Mother of God herself. There is such human under-standing of their problems, and instructions and advice which can only be termed divine, for it undoubtedly descended from that source.

It would be disproportionate to quote all her letters to these two men, but that would undoubtedly be the best way of con-veying the sacrosanct tenderness and wisdom Thérèse had ar-rived at at this period, the closing years of her life.

As it is, we must do what we can by our own inadequate account of it.

She has suddenly become mature. She is twenty-three, and she is a woman. The childlike heart is the same, and there are still occasional touches of that almost coy naïveté to which she was addicted, but in the main what she writes now to these two spiritual brothers has the depth and calm of one who has entered into the peace of an infinite comprehension of reality. She looks *down* on the world.

For those of us who are still struggling with our conflicts, and whose natural desires still predominate, those of us who are still vainly seeking fulfilment here below, it is indeed often difficult to accept her wisdom. Her point of view is ex-asperating to us, but the truth of it compels us even when we are tired of the effort, and even if we cannot achieve it in actuality (we can in any case, of ourselves, achieve nothing) we must try at least to dispose of that natural sense of gravity which seems for ever to be resisting grace and pulling us back, and go and stand with her, if only in imagination, on the summit of her mountain.

It is clear now she has always regarded this life as a means to heaven, and never as an end in itself. Indeed, it would seem sometimes that she had not appreciated the beauties of our earthly existence sufficiently. But she was disillusioned so early.

When she was little more than a baby, sitting on the bank watching her father fishing, and the time came for them to eat their sandwiches, the white bread, so fresh and inviting when they set out, had become dry and curled up, and it was immediately an example to her of the perishable pleasures of the world. That at four years of age!

No, if we are to imbibe the nourishment she has to give us, we must rise to where she is on wings of love. We may not be able to remain in that rarefied air for long—indeed, we almost certainly shall not—but we shall surely bring something back with us, a little touch of gold, a hope, an intimation of better things in store. . . .

With Thérèse the soul comes first; with most of us it is the body, which we may take to include all the natural attributes of the pride of life, the senses, and the intellect. It is the outcome of the fall of man. We stand with our backs to God, and no efforts of ours can wrench the being round to face Him, it can only be done through the gift of His grace. Thus it is often against our inclination to see things from the saint's point of view, for it seems to imply, erroneously but insistently, a complete renunciation of every thing which makes existence on this earth worth while. Perversely we do not want the promises of Christ, and yet it is in them our true happiness will consist.

But when we come to examine her Little Way, we shall see it is not really a matter of straining for perfection, but a humbling of oneself, an abandonment to Love, so that, paradoxically, one may live in conflict and in peace at the same time.

She saw the souls of men glowing. Perhaps what we inadequately term sex-appeal is really just that?

Her own soul was now glowing with a white fire. The "letter," as she termed it, was beginning to shine through the "envelope." But she did not despise the "envelope," even if, as she admitted, she had never, since she could remember, been comfortable in it. She knew it was going to heaven too, where it would be glorified—yes, even poor Brother Ass, as another saint had called it, was going to be transmuted and honored and made more lovely than an apotheosis of all the most beautiful forms in the world.

But we are getting away from the theme of the chapter, which is about her relationship with her two invisible friends. It was considered prudent to keep the business a secret and although at recreation Mother Marie Gonzague read aloud to the whole community extracts from the letters of "our two missionaries," nobody knew until after her death, not even her own sisters, that it was little Thérèse who was their real recipient, and the instigator of so much of their interesting contents.

Soon after his ordination, before leaving for China, Père Roulland actually came to the Carmel to say Mass.

Thérèse had made a corporal and a purificator with a pall for him to use at his first Mass, which was celebrated in Paris on the 29th June, 1896.

"For a long time," she wrote to him, "I have desired to know an *apostle* who would *utter my name at the holy Altar on the day of his first Mass*. . . . I desired to prepare the sacred linen myself and the *white Host* destined to veil the King of Heaven." And God had been pleased to fulfil her dream.

We can imagine the tantalizing excitement of their conversation. They were allowed to talk together for the customary half-hour in the parlor, hidden from each other of course by the black-shrouded grille.

She did receive Holy Communion at his hands, and saw for an instant his consecrated finger and thumb protruding through the little *guichet* by the side of the High Altar just before he popped the Sacred Host into her mouth. But perhaps she denied herself that sensible pleasure, and refused to look. We do not know.

Well, there he was, her new brother, only two years older than herself, so near she could have touched him, and soon to be thousands of miles away, their only contact haphazard bits of paper, more than one of which would disintegrate in the Blue River. "Ah! how long must we wait till we have no need of ink and paper to tell one another our thoughts," she sighed.

Just before he sailed he was given permission to send her a photograph. Again Mother Marie's seeming harshness was tempered by a gesture of kindliness, attributable to a sweeter nature than she was supposed to possess. Carmelites were not usually allowed to own even pictures of their relations. But one morning the Prioress arrived at Thérèse's cell with the precious piece of pasteboard. "Will you keep this in our writing-case," she said, her stern eyes screwed up humorously. "We will take it back when necessary." But she never took it back.

We have not been able to see this likeness, so the reader is at liberty to fill it in from his or her own imagination. Was he handsome and shiny-eyed as a young missionary might be depicted by those who prefer their heroes to look it, or had he the typical uninspired appearance of the *petit bourgeois,* the light of his crusading spirit masked by conventional dullness, and a pair of pince-nez perhaps? It did not matter to Thérèse what he looked like, but she was a woman, and if there were signs of nobility in his physiognomy she was doubtless delighted to remark them.

A map of the province of Su Chuen was obtained—Another of her Mother's sympathetic touches?—but she would not have this piece of too fascinating exoticism in her cell. She pinned it up in the common-room where all might enjoy it.

It was not long before she wrote and asked her brother to send her a list of the principal dates in his life. She had always been interested in spiritual milestones, her own and other people's. And from this she learned an interesting coincidence. Coincidence? No, it was something much more significant than that.

It appears that on the 8th September, 1890, the day of Thérèse's Profession, young Roulland had reached a crisis of doubt. For some time he had been uncertain of his vocation—his endurance of the baptism of fire in the world was proving too arduous—and, almost despairingly, he had, on that day, forced himself to make a pilgrimage to the well-known Normandy shrine of Notre Dame de la Déliverande. Kneeling in prayer there, his uncertainty suddenly vanished. He knew without doubt his idea of becoming a missionary was no romantic personal dream, but a definite call from Almighty God.

Thérèse, on learning this, was absolutely certain his vocation had been saved by Mary, Queen of Apostles and Martyrs. On that very day, perhaps at the very hour of the young man's struggle, she had asked the Mother of God to give her the soul of a priest.

She was by now in correspondence with the Abbé Bellière, who had been unsettled by his military service, so she wrote immediately to Père Roulland to ask him to pray that God would grant a similar light to his spiritual brother.

She had recently read the life of Blessed Théophane Vénard, a young missionary—a gay smiler like herself—who had been killed during the course of his labors, and again the attractions of death for the Faith cropped up. She hoped it might happen to her, considered it possible owing to the religious uncertainties of the time, but these had undoubtedly been exaggerated by parlor gossip.

It was, of course, the quickest way to Heaven. (She was very literal; St. Francis was hardly more so.) But Father Roulland must have found it a little disconcerting, to say the least of it, to receive as a New Year's Greeting best wishes for his speedy martyrdom!

She admitted herself it was rather unusual. But she persisted in her prayers for him to that effect. However, God did not demand that sacrifice, however meritorious, from everyone, and saw fit to temper his advocate's zeal by allowing Père Roulland to die a natural death at an age not far short of the allotted three score years and ten.

Nevertheless, she was sure he was going to be a saint, and begged for a relic in the shape of a scrap of his hair, which had been cut off during the process of changing the style of his coiffure from European to Asian. The authorities had considered it would be helpful to the cause of Christianity if he were to proselytize in a pigtail.

She received the lock of hair, also his visiting-card in Chinese. This latter object amused and fascinated her very much, for she never knew if she had it right side up or upside down!

As well as spiritual comfort and admonitions they exchanged entertaining anecdotes. Thérèse wrote and told him about the "possessed" lobster. Although the sight of a hen sheltering its chicks beneath its wings had reminded her of God's protection of mankind in such an overpoweringly emotional manner that she had had to be led away "all imbued with tears," there was nothing sentimental in the way she described the vicissitudes of the poor shellfish which had refused to be contained in the seething pot, so that a simple lay-sister on kitchen duty had rushed to the Prioress convinced the refractory animal was in the grip of an evil spirit.

Thérèse recounts the incident right down to the clamping on of the saucepan-lid and the eventual eating of the innocent creature with an ironical gusto, which those inclined to an excessive love of animals might regard as heartless. It was the Normandy realism in her character. Animals, however they might serve as examples of patience and forbearance, were intended for a repast for men, and it was useless pretending otherwise. So the lobster's natural inclination to leap out of the boiling water, thus causing an ignorant girl to regard it as "possessed" was an occasion of merriment to her.

It was at about this time that there was talk of sending her to Tonking, and she liked to write to her "brother" about it, although of course the idea was a quite impracticable one. In Mother Marie Gonzague's opinion, and she was undoubtedly right, the scabbard was not strong enough to contain the sword and might have had to have been cast into the sea *en route*. Still, the fact that she had been asked for did help her more and more to identify her own fervor with those whose abiding enthusiasm was the conversion of the heathen.

He wrote to her of one of his first converts, a little girl. "Shall I baptize her Marie or Thérèse?" he asked. She decided on the name of the Queen of Heaven without cogitation. The name of the illustrious Mother of Carmel was very beautiful, but she had no intention of suggesting it before that of the Mother of God. That "Thérèse" referred to herself, and not to the Spanish St. Teresa of Avila, had apparently not occurred to her; but she did ask that when the occasion arose again he baptize two girls with the names of Céline and Thérèse in memory of herself and Sister Geneviève, who had been Céline in the world.

She informed him of her parents' great desire to produce a missionary in their family, and how the male issue God had sent them had all died in infancy, but, because he was her "brother," she felt sure their wish had been granted in Heaven, and that now they would be enjoying watching over the progress of a son that had been born to them, after, as it were, their departure from the earth.

As for herself, despite her longing to help him, she knew she was nothing, a "little zero," but if nought was added on the right side of the integer its power was increased ten times.

They were both babies, anyway. Was it not evident? He was only just learning to talk (in Chinese) and she (because of the diet prescribed at that time by the doctors) was able to imbibe nothing but milk. These droll circumstances were surely an indication of her Little Way, which she was at some pains to teach to both her brothers, for she was becoming more and more convinced of its efficacy, and that it was her duty to communicate it to all souls who crossed her path.

2

We come now to her correspondence with her younger spiritual brother, the twenty-two-year-old Abbé Bellière. His was perhaps a more complicated character than that of his compatriot, and these difficult traits of sensitivity and temperament must have touched echoing chords in the heart of Thérèse, for, as we have seen, her own simplicity had not come naturally to her, but had been arrived at by binding all her idiosyncrasies and scruples, the delicate flowers and bitter-scented herbs of her spirituality, into a bouquet of praises. She had become integrated through offering everything to God.

The Abbé Bellière was young, passionate, impressionable, perhaps, with the highest aspirations, and an abrasive regret for his failure to live always on the peaks. She sympathized with him in her first letter—the first, that is, that is extant. There are ten letters in existence from him, and six from Père Roulland.

"The fact is," she wrote, "that when Jesus calls a man to guide and save multitudes of other souls, it is most necessary that He make him experience the temptations and trials of life." And later: "I confess, Brother, that you and I do not see Heaven in quite the same way. It seems to you that, participating in the justice and holiness of God, I shall not be able, as on earth, to excuse your faults. Are you forgetting that I shall also be participating in the *infinite mercy* of the Lord? I believe that the Blessed in Heaven have a great compassion for our wretchedness; they remember that when they were frail and mortal like us they committed the same faults, endured the same struggles, and their fraternal love becomes

greater even than it was on earth, which is why they do not
cease to protect us and pray for us."

As for herself, it would have been hypocritical in her to
have owned to sins such as theirs which she had never committed. What she did admit was the possibility in her of committing everybody's sins, and her thanks were to God for having spared her beforehand by removing the temptations. Thus
she had little to expiate, and she knew it. Her deliberate mortification by the life of Carmel was for the sins of others. But
it was love, and love alone, even so. She had not incarcerated
herself to "climb the rough road of fear," but to rise *via* "the
lift of love," and to suffer with confidence and joy. Indeed, she
remarked that the fact of her being happy in heaven was puz-
zling to her, for it implied bliss without pain, a condition
which seemed, strange child, completely alien to her soul's
exigencies.

No doubt that year the crude camaraderie of the army had
suggested an existence to the young man other than that of a
vocation to the priesthood, and it was taking a little time to
shut out from his mind the seemingly delectable pictures of
laissez-faire and unchastity offered him by the gaiety and youth-
ful brutishness of his wine-bibbing and love-making companions. He was very conscious of the coarseness of being a
man, and Thérèse seemed to him at first a remote Beatrician
ideal of young womanhood. But she refused to be placed on a
pedestal, insisted immediately on the intimacy of sharing each
other's burdens. She too was human, was only too aware of
her common human frailties. It did not matter. What mattered
was the all-embracing love of God. The "martyrdom of the
heart" was very terrible to bear in the beginning, but she knew
by this time it could be, paradoxically, the source of unutterable
joy.

It was an agonizing wrench for the young priest to leave
the comfort and security of his home, and separate himself

from the warmth and affection of his family by leagues of remorseless sea and wastes of desert.

Yes, of course, had she not experienced a similar desola-
tion that tear-misted morning so long ago when the gate of
Les Buissonnets had clicked gently but irrevocably behind her,
and she had walked down the familiar garden-strewn hill on
her good father's arm for the last time?

She assured him of her prayres for his mother, reminded
him of the mortified grief of the Mother of Jesus, who had
stood at the foot of the cross with an invisible sword in her
heart. But that unspeakable misery was only in time. In Eternity
all the mothers and sons of God's loved ones would be re-
united and together always.

We learn from her next letter, which is dated 24th February, that she is still working as sacristan. She must by this time
have been very ill. By the summer she could hide the seriousness of it no longer.

In this letter we discover the Abbé's Christian name—Maurice. It is on this occasion that he, too, is asked for his list of
dates!—and receives hers in return.

Their souls grow closer and closer with each communication,
althought Thérèse is always careful to express her feelings and
ideas with a delicacy that no one, neither her superiors in religion, nor the opinionated of the world, can take objection to.
Their courtesies are like those of a lady and her knight, so that
one sees in imagination a feminine figure waving from a medieval turret as an armored male, caparisoned with the cross, his
steel arm bound with her handkerchief, rides off on the plains
below to tourney in the distant crusades.

Thérèse compares them both to Blessed Margaret Mary of
the devotion to the Sacred Heart and her beloved friend and
confessor, the Venerable Père de la Colombière, not that she
considers they have by any means attained to such heights of
sanctity, but that like the other more famous couple they are
united by similar sympathies in the same cause.

She feels she just cannot go on calling him "Monsieur L'Abbé"—it makes him seem even farther removed, and so formal; so Mother Marie Gonzague gives her permission to address him in the same terms as she speaks of him to Jesus. Thus for the rest of their too short correspondence she refers to him frankly as her "brother."

Brother Maurice, apparently, did not need to be encouraged into a state of mind desirous of martyrdom. He had the wish already, and asked Thérèse to pray that it should come about. She quotes St. Paul to him: "It is not of him that wills, nor of him that runs, but of God that shows mercy," but of course agrees with alacrity to pray for his intention, hoping, as she says, that since her Lord seems willing to grant her only the martyrdom of love, he will allow her to gather the other palm of her ambition through him. (It may be mentioned here that the palm-leaf placed in her coffin was intact and still green at the exhumation, and is preserved with her other relics in the Lisieux Carmel.) Even so, despite her earnest endeavors to have it otherwise, the Abbé Bellière, although admittedly young enough to excite a pious sympathy, will die peacefully in the old carved family bed at Langrunes.

In June Thérèse feels her own death is imminent, and suddenly conveys her earthly farewells, ending the letter with a touching colloquialism. It reads like the final phrase of a letter any girl might have written to her fiancé just before going off to take up some duty in the capital, at which important place her lover will join her after a few months or years of necessary separation. "See you soon," she concludes, "I'll see you in Heaven!"

But the time was not quite yet. The dark angel, still watching her, drew back into the shadows and the letter did not have to be sent.

They resume their precious paper conversations, talking now of God's love for sinners, and how in many cases those who had been known for great sinners had, after their conversion, become some of the most famous saints. For those of us who are often near despairing that we shall never be able to shake off our hampering frailties, it is encouraging to think of those passionate beings who ultimately changed all their desires, however worldly or sensual, into vibrating flames of purest love. Yes, we may build our hopes on the sins of the saints. . . .

"Ah! my Brother," she writes, "like me you can hymn the mercies of the Lord! They shine in you in all their splendor . . . you love St. Augustine, St. Magdalen, those souls to whom 'many sins have been forgiven because they loved much'; I love them too, love their repentence, and above all . . . their daring in love! When I see Magdalen come forward in face of the crowd of guests, and water with tears the feet of her adored Master as she touches Him for the first time, I feel that *her heart* realized the fathomless depths of love and mercy in Jesus' Heart, realized despite her sins that that Heart was ready not only to pardon her but actually to lavish on her the treasures of His divine intimacy and raise her to the highest summits of contemplation."

Until the very last—she had less than two months to go now —her letters were replete with cheerfulness and hope. "I am like a finch," she told him, and indeed it was so. As the pen failed her, and eventually the only slightly less irksome pencil also, the bird-notes became purer and clearer, until the pean of praise was too sheer to be transmitted to paper; but in one of her rare resurgences of energy she was able to write him a letter which is so typical of her at her best that we cannot forbear quoting it in full.

It is beautifully expressed, and contains one of those delicious instances of twinkling Thérèsian humor, an example of that mischievous Carmelite gaiety which touches the austere cold passages of their convents like a ripple of winter sunshine. He has asked her a question, and she makes him wait, so delicately, so tantalizingly, for his answer until the very last line:

"My dear little Brother,

"What pleasure your letter gave me! If Jesus has heard your prayers and prolonged my exile a little, He has also heard mine, since you are resigned to losing 'my presence, my visible action,' as you say. Ah! Brother, let me tell you: the good God has many a sweet surprize in store for your soul. You write that it is 'not much habituated to supernatural things'; and I, who am not your little sister for nothing, promise when I have gone into life everlasting to make you taste the joy that lies in feeling a friend's soul close at hand. It will not be an exchange of letters —more or less remote, always so very incomplete—which you seem to regret losing; it will be a conversation of brother and sister which will delight the Angels, a conversation of which creatures cannot disapprove, for it will be hidden from them.

"Ah! how good it will feel to be delivered from this mortal body, which would oblige me—if *by an impossibility* I were in my dear little brother's company when others were present—to treat him as a stranger, one who meant nothing to me! . . .

"Please, Brother, do not follow the example of the Hebrews, who look back with longing to 'the onions of Egypt.' For long I have served you only too many of those vegetables which make you *weep* when you bring them, raw, too near your eyes. Now I dream of sharing with you 'the hidden manna' (Apocalpse) that the Almighty has promised 'the victors.' Precisely because it is *hidden* this heavenly *manna* attracts less than 'the onions of Egypt,' but, I am certain, once I am permitted to offer you a wholly spiritual food, you will never more regret the food I would have given you, had I still remained long on earth.

"Ah! your soul is too great to be attached to any joy of earth! You must live by anticipation in Heaven, for it is said 'where a man's heart is, there is his treasure.' Is not your *sole* treasure Jesus? Since he is in Heaven that is where your heart must dwell. And I tell you quite simply, dear little Brother, I feel it will be easier for you to live with Jesus when I am with Him for ever.

"You must know me very imperfectly, to fear that a detailed account of your faults would lessen my affection for your soul. O Brother! do believe I shall not need to 'put my hand over Jesus' mouth.' He has long forgotten your infidelities, only your desires for perfection are present to give joy to his Heart.

"Please, I beg you, never again *'drag yourself to his feet,'* follow the 'first impulse which would draw you into his arms'; that is where you belong, and I see, even more clearly than in your other letters, that you are *barred* from going to Heaven by any other way than your poor little sister's.

"I am altogether of your opinion that 'the Divine Heart is more grieved at the thousand small discourtesies of His friends than by the faults, even the grave faults, committed by people in the world'; but, dear little Brother, surely it is *only* when his friends, not noticing their repeated discourtesy, let it become habitual, and do not ask pardon, that Jesus can say the touching words that are put into the Church's mouth during Holy Week: 'The wounds in the midst of my hands are those I received in the house of them that loved me.' For those who love Him and, after each discourteous act, cast themselves into His arms and ask pardon, Jesus is vibrant with joy. He says to His angels what the prodigal son's father said to his servants: 'Put on him the first robe, put a ring on his hand, and let us make merry.' Ah! Brother, how little are Jesus' *kindness* and *merciful love* realized! . . . It is true that, to enjoy his riches, we must humble ourselves, see our own nothingness, which is what many souls will not do; but, little Brother, you do not act like them, so the way of simple loving confidence is indeed the way for you. I would have you to be *simple* with the good God—and with me too. You are startled at that phrase? I say it, dear little Brother, because you ask me to *forgive* 'your indiscretion' in wanting to know if *your sister's* name in the world was Geneviève. Actually the question strikes me as perfectly natural. To prove it, I am going to give you details about my family, for you have not been told a great deal.

"God gave me a father and mother worthier of Heaven than earth. They asked the Lord to give them many children and take them for Himself. Their desire was fulfilled. Four little angels fled away to Heaven, and the five children who remained in the arena took Jesus for their Spouse. It was with heroic courage that my father, like another Abraham, three times climbed the mountain of Carmel to immolate to God the thing he held most dear. First were his two eldest; then his third daughter, on the advice of her director, was taken by her incomparable father to try her vocation in a Visitation Convent. . . . There remained only two children to God's Elect, one eighteen, the other fourteen. The latter, 'little Thérèse,' asked his permission to fly off to Carmel: she gained it without difficulty, and her good father in his limitless kindness took her first to Bayeux, then to Rome, to remove the obstacles in the way of the immediate immolation of one whom he called *his Queen.* When he had brought her to the gate, he said to the *one child* remaining to him: 'If you want to follow your sister's example, I consent, don't bother about me.'

"The angel who was to support the old age of such a saint answered him that *when he had gone to Heaven* she too would take flight to the cloister, which filled him with joy, for he lived for God alone.

"But so beautiful a life required to be crowned by a trial worthy of it. A little after my departure, the father we had such good reason to love was seized by paralysis in the legs: such a trial would have been too easy, for the heroic patriarch had *offered himself to God as a victim:* so the paralysis changed its course and lodged in the venerable head of the *victim* whom the Lord had accepted. . . .

"I have no room for the moving details, I need only say that we had to drink the chalice to the dregs: we were separated from our venerated father for three years, confiding him to the hands of religious, indeed, but strangers.

"He accepted the trial, realizing all its humiliation, and carried heroism to the point of wanting us not to pray for a cure.

"Goodbye, dear little Brother, I hope to write to you again unless the shaking of my hand grows worse, for I have been forced to write this letter with many pauses between.

> "Your little sister, not Geneviève, but 'Thérèse' of
> the Child Jesus of the Holy Face."

He asked her if she had become his sister by choice. She answered yes, not admitting, in order to save his feelings doubtless, that it had not been her own choice but the choice of her superiors.

He begged that she would leave him some little token to remember her by. Everything Carmelites possess is owned in common, so she was not free to grant his request. But Mother Marie Gonzague said he might inherit her crucifix.

It was a very small legacy, of no intrinsic value. But it was a symbol of consuming Love. She had kissed the face almost entirely away. . . .

CHAPTER THREE

✼

The Little Way

I

THE TIME HAS come now to reveal the secret of the sanctity of St. Thérèse.

It will have been remarked that during the course of this work several allusions have been made to the "Little Way." The "little" way was the method, if a manner of life so unperemptory could be termed such, which Thérèse discovered for herself. It was a path that was to lead her directly into the Heart of God, and it was founded on an attitude of mind which she refers to as the state of "Spiritual Childhood."

It was not a system. It could hardly be described as logical. There are no complicated rules, and those who follow it are under no necessity to sink their personalities in a common mould. It is for everyone, and for everyone it is different. That is to say, once the principles have been applied, the soul may go forward untrammelled by fettering conventions, free, spontaneous, and vividly individual. That is what is so attractive about it—its utter lack of constraint.

It was the fatherhood of God that appealed particularly to Thérèse. And what more natural when her earthly father had been the epitome of paternal affection? All the Martin girls, though there was some deviation in the case of the mysterious Léonie, had that reliance on their parents which springs from an upbringing in a happy home. So it was not a question of compensation, but an extension, to infinite proportions, of the earthly human love which had been lavished upon her by Monsieur Martin.

A nun having occasion to enter Thérèse's cell one evening

found her lost in contemplation, her sewing fallen in her lap. "What are you doing?" she was asked. "I am saying the Our Father," came the reply, and suddenly the far-away eyes filled with an expression of ineffable tenderness. "How lovely it is to think of God as our father."

The Our Father is a common prayer, well-known alike to professing Christians and many who have not received the gift of Faith, yet how many really do regard God as a father, as their father? There are millions who are only aware of him as a sort of magistrate or, in many cases of miserable superstition which pass for religion, as an all-powerful spirit, capricious and terrifying, to be placated, if possible, by incessant burnt-offerings.

But Thérèse knew the Almighty was, quite simply (don't let us be afraid of the sentiment of the colloquilism), her heavenly papa. If we cannot stomach this expression, if we find it audacious, or merely silly, as applied to the omniscient omnipotent Creator, then we shall be too clever to understand the "Little Way." There are divine truths to which intellectuality has no access—"Out of the mouths of babes . . . ". The various childhood texts are of course correlative. If God is our father, we are His children.

Thérèse, as she flitted about the scriptures (*"elle butinait,"* as the nuns of Carmel described her haphazard reading), alighted on many of these texts, and settled there, imbibing a nourishment in keeping with her pure simplicity. She took what they had to say quite literally.

"Amen, I say unto you, unless you be converted and become as little children you shall not enter into the kingdom of Heaven."

"Whosoever, therefore, shall humble himself as this little child, he will be the greatest in the kingdom of Heaven."

"Suffer the little ones to come unto Me, for of such is the kingdom of Heaven."

"Amen, I say unto you, whosoever shall not receive the kingdom of God as a little child shall not enter into it."

These are the words of Jesus Christ, Himself. They are clear. Not all the sayings of Our Lord were so, nor those of his apostles. Theological doctors and laymen alike will crack their heads over the Epistles of St. Paul until the end of time. But there can be no gainsaying the above.

We do not really need to inquire into them, for their meaning is self-evident. Nevertheless their simple truth is often forgotten, hidden under the great heap of Christian dialectics which has piled up so confusingly since the, to many of us, doubtless, unimaginable first days of God's early ministry, when the Word was made flesh and dwelt among us, preaching and performing miracles, convincing, or not convincing, by the living presence of His divine personality.

Perhaps if we had heard Him say those words Himself they would have remained stamped indelibly on our souls for ever. Thérèse did hear Him. And she believed. And she acted accordingly. She became a child of God.

The result was, as might have been expected, a secure and serene confidence.

Do we remember, really remember, what it was like to be a child? Not just the incidents, but the true ambience of childhood, when the little organism, like an innocent bird or butterfly, took spontaneous delight in its capacities, when the unrealized memory of Eden joys hovered over us like a brightness, when all was to be hoped for, and fleshly passions and ambitions had not risen to dominate, to sully, and to delude.

But that was not my childhood, you may say. That is the dream of a sentimentalist. I was treated unfairly; I had hates; I was vicious; or it was all rather dull.

But underneath all that? Before the glacier of regret descended. Wasn't it just as we have said? Did not joy sometimes break from your heart like a bubble or star? And the freshness of everything, the newness, the sense of adventure, the crammed moment that knew nothing of time . . . ?

Poets remember more constantly; every man remembers in

flashes, perhaps when one is very old one remembers it all. . . .

But Thérèse had never forgotten. She practised the presence of God in the trusting unselfconscious way a child behaves to its father. It was this which gave her so much daring, disposing of that disproportionate fear of sin which narrows and confines so many professing Christians in a claustrophobic prison-house. A loving father is always forgiving. As she wrote to the Abbé Bellière, supposing there were two naughty children, which would be more likely to win its father's approval, the one who huddled timorously in a corner afraid to confess, or the one who flung itself into its parent's arms, protesting its sorrow, promising never to do "it" again, knowing at the same time that it would hardly be able to keep its promise, but contrite nevertheless? The latter child's punishment, she said, would be a kiss.

We are bound to sin. It is our nature to do so. If it were possible to live without sinning, why has God instituted the sacrament of Penance? And yet there are some souls, proud, but well-intentioned no doubt, who seem to think frailty a kind of failure, and that one should strain to live so as to have nothing to confess. One should never strain, and, made as we are, it would be impossible to have nothing to confess. Thérèse knew her Father understood, and asked not that His child should be perfect, except according to His Grace—the only way —but that she should be sorry and remain confident in loving.

Such an attitude, coming when and where it did, was revolutionary. It has shocked some. It is still not properly understood. But it has become an acceptable, a fruitful way of life to millions. Why is this? Because it takes our humanity into account, whereas so many religious systems seem to leave it out, and the poor creature grows weary and despairing because it is being continually admonished to a state of spiritual perfection seeming beyond its reach.

We know that sin is negative, although it was St. Augustine who referred to certain "happy faults," as he called them. But

Thérèse, by demonstrating her Little Way, has shown that it is possible to turn all our sins to good account. What other saint has had the adorable temerity to say just that?

St. Thérèse knew that, according to the scriptures, we could not call God our father without possessing the Spirit of Love, so she asked the saints for a *double portion* of their love of Him. "I dare not try to understand all that my prayer means, O my God! I should fear to be crushed by the mere weight of its audacity. That I am thy *child* is my only excuse, for children do not grasp the full meaning of their words. Yet, if their parents were to mount a throne and inherit vast wealth, they would not hesitate to grant the desires of their little ones, who are dearer to them than life itself. To please them they would spend most lavishly, stooping even to weakness."

2

There were three Popes associated with the cause of St. Thérèse. Pius X introduced it in June 1914. Benedict XV declared her Venerable in August 1921, and she was Beatified in April 1923 and finally Canonized in May 1925 by Pius XI. The Little Way was approved and recommended by them all.

On the occasion of the Promulgation of the Decree concerning her virtues, Pope Benedict XV made an allocution in which the state of "Spiritual Childhood" was held up before the faithful as an example of sanctification which anyone might follow, not only heroic souls like herself but the weakest sinners:

"The harmony which exists between body and mind renders it possible for the former to furnish a basis for the explanation of the characteristics of Spiritual Childhood. Observe a child as yet uncertain of its steps, and without the use of speech. If pursued by another child of its own age, or threatened by a stronger child, or terrified by the unexpected sight of some animal, whither does it run for safety? Where does it seek a refuge? On its mother's breast. Shielded in her arms, and clasped to her bosom, all its fears vanish, and with a deep sigh it faces, not only fearlessly but even daringly, the object of its former terror and distress, as though it would say: 'Now I am sure of help. I fling myself with confidence into my mother's arms, not only to be safeguarded from all enemy attacks, but to be there where I can gather strength.' In the same way Spiritual Childhood is the result of trust in God and complete abandonment to Him.

"It will not be out of place to enumerate the qualities of this Spiritual Childhood, both as regards what it omits and what it includes. It knows nothing of self-pride, or the thought of being able to attain by purely natural means a supernatural end, or those spurious notions of self-reliance in the hour of danger and temptation. On the other hand, it presupposes a lively faith in the existence of God, a practical homage to His power and mercy, a confident recourse to the providence of Him who alone can give us grace to avoid evil and seek good. Thus, whether regarded from the negative or the positive point of view, the qualities which comprise Spiritual Childhood evoke our admiration, and enable us to realize why Our Lord Jesus Christ pointed to it as a necessary condition for obtaining eternal life. . . .

"The Son of God was not content with merely stating that the kingdom of Heaven was for children—'For of such is the kingdom of Heaven'—or that whosoever should become as a little child would be greatest in the kingdom of Heaven. He went so far as to exclude from His Kingdom those who did not become as little children. Now, when a master adopts various methods to inculcate the same lesson, does he not thereby seek to emphasize its value in his sight? If Jesus Christ used so many devices to drive home this lesson to His disciples, it is because He wishes, by one means or another, to insure their thorough understanding of it. From this we must conclude it was the Divine Master's express desire that His disciples should see that the way of Spiritual Childhood is the path which leads to eternal life.

"In face of this insistent and forcible teaching of Our Lord, there would surely not be a soul that could hesitate to enter this way of confidence and self-surrender—all the more so, to repeat our own words, because Our Divine Lord, not only in a general manner, but also by a concrete example, declared this way of life to be absolutely essential, even in the case of those who have lost the innocence of their childhood. There are some who try to persuade themselves that the way of trust and abandonment to God is the exclusive privilege of those souls whose baptismal robe has remained unsullied by sin. They are unable to reconcile the idea of Spiritual Childhood with the loss of their innocence. But do not the words of the Divine Master, *'Unless ye be converted and become as little children,'* indicate the necessity of a change, and, consequently, the effort to effect that change? 'Unless ye be converted' suggests a transformation which the disciples of Jesus had to undergo in order to become children once again; and who should become a child again, if not he who is no longer one? 'Unless ye become as little children'—carry with them the obligation to labor to regain the lost qualities of childhood. It would be absurd to dream of resuming either the outward appearance or feebleness of the state of infancy, but it is not unreasonable to discern, in the words of the Gospel, a counsel given to those who have attained maturity to return to the virtues associated with Spiritual Childhood. . . .

"Through the designs of Providence she was placed under the patronage of the Child Jesus, who thus showed His pleasure at her faithful endeavor to honor the virtues of His infancy. Let us add, moreover, that this new title served as a fresh incentive to the Holy Carmelite to abandon herself more entirely to God. She pictured to herself the ever-docile Child of Bethlehem in the arms of His most holy Mother, ready to let himself be borne from Bethlehem to Egypt, and from Egypt to Nazareth. Thérèse, in her turn, placed herself in the arms of the holy rule of Carmel, allowing herself to be guided in every-thing by religious obedience. With the eyes of her soul she saw the Divine Worker of Nazareth always fulfilling tasks allotted to Him by His adopted father, always submissive to those who stood to Him in the place of His Heavenly Father. In imitation of His example, Thérèse diligently carried out the orders of her Prioress and Novice Mistress, and this she did perfectly, with-out complaint or remark of any nature, as though possessing no will of her own. So brightly did there shine in this young Car-melite the virtues of the Infant Saviour that, if by a dispensa-tion of Providence the title 'of the Child Jesus' had not fallen to her lot, her Sisters in religion would have bestowed it upon her. When one day the Infant Saviour appeared to her holy Mother of Avila, and on asking her name received from the saintly Reformer the reply, 'I am called Teresa of Jesus,' she merited to hear this answer: 'And I am Jesus of Teresa.' In like manner Sœur Thérèse of Lisieux could declare: 'I am called Thérèse of the Child Jesus because the Child Jesus is the Mas-ter and the Model of Thérèse.' "

But let us see what Thérèse herself had to say about it. We should need considerably more than the space available in this chapter to tabulate all the references she made to the easy efficacy of the Way of Spiritual Childhood. It seems there was no one with whom she was brought in contact who did not learn something of the method to which she was so devoted.

To a novice who had lost heart at the thought of her im-perfections she remarked: "You remind me of a little child just learning how to stand on its feet, yet determined to climb a flight of stairs in order to find its mother. Time after time it tires to set its tiny foot upon the lowest step, and each time it stumbles and falls. . . . Do as that little one did. By the practice of all the virtues keep on lifting your foot to climb the ladder of perfection, but do not imagine you can yourself succeed in mounting even the very first step. God asks of you nothing but goodwill. From the top of the ladder He looks down lovingly;

and presently, touched by your fruitless efforts, He will take you in His arms to His kingdom, never to be parted from Him again. But if you leave off lifting your foot, your stay on the ground will indeed be a long one."

When temptations seem irrestible, and not to be overcome, her advice is to undergo: "It's all very well for great souls to soar above the clouds when the storm bursts. We have simply to stand in the rain. What does it matter if we get wet? We can dry ourselves in the sunshine of love."

In connection with the advantages of remaining small, she was reminded of an incident in her childhood. A horse had strayed out of a nearby field, and was blocking the gateway of Les Buissonnets. The sisters stood timorously debating how they might get past, or how the refractory animal could be persuaded to move. Meantime Thérèse slipped between its legs. It is difficult to know exactly what she intended by this analogy. It does not follow that just because one is small there are loopholes for escape. Though, one supposes, humility would take one unscathed through a temptation, just as the little pinafored mite passed quickly and easily under the belly of the horse. But temptations are not always as four-square as that animal. The way under is not always so obvious. Still, there is something in it. It seems one would also have to be very quick, very daring. . . .

Towards the end, she was asked: "'Tell us what we must do to be *as little children*. What do you mean by *keeping little?*"

She answered: "When we keep little we recognize our own nothingness and expect everything from the goodness of God, exactly as a little child expects everything from its father. Nothing worries us, not even the amassing of spiritual riches. . . . Again, being as a little child with God means that we do not attribute to ourselves the virtues we may possess, in the belief that we are capable of something. It implies, on the contrary, our recognition of the fact that God places the treasure of virtue in the hand of His little child for him to use as he needs it, though all the while it is God's treasure.

"Finally, to *keep little* means not to lose courage at the sight of our faults. Little children often tumble, but they are too small to suffer grievous injury."

That she was under no misapprehension as to the difference between childish and childlike will be seen from the following: "The Holy Innocents are not infants in heaven, they only have the indefinable charms of childhood. They are represented as children merely because we have need of images in order to comprehend invisible things."

In a letter to Léonie she repeats the analogy of the two children, adding: "In the time of the law of fear, before the coming of Our Lord, the prophet Isaias, speaking in the name of the King of Heaven, could say: 'Can a mother forget her child? And if she should forget, yet will not I forget thee.'"

So much for the foundation of the Little Way—the fatherhood of God, and the childhood of mankind.

3

In its practice Thérèse put great stress on the expression "little." This word seems to have an irritant effect on certain strong-minded souls who object to almost every form of diminutive as being sentimental. But, surely, it is a question of proportion. There would be something very absurd if we were to go round coyly referring to ourselves as "little me." That would not be the Little Way at all. What makes such an attitude ridiculous is the implication, the mock humility. When a person says "little me" like that they are unconsciously comparing themselves to other people. When Thérèse referred to herself as little, she was comparing herself to Almighty God. No wonder she wanted to squeeze herself into less than a "grain of sand!" A moment's thought, and it will surely be agreed that compared to the size of the Creator, the very planet we inhabit is probably no more than a dust-speck. In that case how big, or how little, are we? The question is hardly deserving of an answer. We need have no compunction in referring to ourselves as small.

But this stress on littleness in the way of Thérèse was really an expression of her magnanimous charity. It was to encourage us not to be afraid of offering Him our poor all—the widow's mite, in fact. It will be remembered that when Thérèse felt she possessed nothing, she was not above offering that nothing to God. And she tells us to do the same. To pick up a pin for love.

The fabric of her life is composed of the tiniest chips, the result a glorious mosaic. She did nothing remarkable, and now she is renowned.

She knew her body, unlike those of other saints, would, when it was exhumed, present merely a handful of dust. She told her sisters that. "If it were to be intact," she said, "it would not be in keeping with my Little Way." The example she has set us seems, deceptively no doubt, so easy to follow. It is to reassure us.

She soon gave up any attempt at extraordinary mortification, preferring little things, like checking a hasty word or look or thought. She allowed herself to be exacerbated by the day's irritations, so that when the time came for her to suffer so extremely that it is beyond our imaginations—though there was nothing dramatic about it, no racks, no wheels, no public demonstration of martyrdom—she was ready, and passed through the fire with the same cheerful simplicity. One of her few deliberate pains was to drink her bitter medicine slowly. If she had thought about it she might have decided even that was too ostentatious. She would be satisfied if we drank ours straight up-and-down.

To answer when the bell rang was, in her opinion, more meritorious than writing pious books. It was the intention behind everything that changed the bits of flint to glittering inlay, the prosaic drudgery to a glorious flight of the spirit. And the intention was love.

If the love of God for man could stoop from heaven to earth, if Christ, himself, could descend into hell, then there could be nothing, no thought or action, too low for man himself to go down to. And in the end everything would be transmuted, raised to be part of the fabric of heaven itself.

It is the whole meaning of humility. If our sins succeed in humbling us, then let them come back again and again. Let Our Father's will be done in all things. We should not judge ourselves. We are here merely to praise and love, and to be loved by Him. It is so simple, so childlike.

Such is the Little Way of St. Thérèse of the Child Jesus. And it may be practised by beggars and kings.

CHAPTER FOUR

❦

Last Words

I

SPRING HAS COME again to the Carmel. Pale daffodil-colored sun hangs in window-oblongs on the white walls of the infirmary. Shadows of new leaves move there, a little tremulous in the fresh airs from which the memory of the snow has not quite faded. The wax-scented floor gleams like lit water.

Old Sister Aimée of Jesus, the infirmarian, rather foolish but eager, sitting far off glueing scapulars, behind a curtain of turning motes, has assumed the matriarchal look of St. Anne.

It is so quiet . . . birds chirping in snatches . . . a bucket clattering in the far-below yard . . . the sound of the gardener's saw . . . Thérèse's cavernous breathing.

She has a bowl of violets, their crisp cushion of heads faceted like a huge sapphire, on the little bedside table. Their scent of cucumber comes in fresh gusts. Flowers, and medicines, and her rubbed crucifix rest upon the Testament and St. Thomas à Kempis. . . .

Some sewing has been put down for a minute. Her fingers resting on the strip of folded-back sheet—she lies so tidily in bed it might be a correctly worn habit—are as green-white and delicate-looking as syringa petals. Held up to the light she can see the bones in them.

"I am turning into a skeleton," she has remarked, laughing. "I like it!"

The flesh was an encumbrance. "My body has always troubled me," she said once. "I have not found myself at ease in it . . . and even when quite a little child it caused me confusion."

189

Through the veils of shine a gilt thread falls, and a little sepia dot of a creature, with febrile bent-in legs thinner than hairs, scrabbles the back of one of her hands. She suffers it to remain as long as it likes, but it is not easy, for she has a feminine horror of spiders. Had, one should say—it is passing away now, for there can be no fear where love is so abundant.

After all, she has acquired a reputation for courage—how, she cannot conceive, for she feels herself to be nothing but a coward—but it will not do to let the world be deceived, so, with the help of grace, she has tried to behave as if she really were the brave young warrior her sisters imagine her to be. It has been the same with the virtue of patience. When complimented on it she exclaimed: "But I have never had it! I have merely tried to behave as if I had."

But as she watches the insect her eyes take on a look of remembered apprehension. She thinks of those awful monthly occasions during her novitiate, when, armed with a long bamboo-handled brush, its head swathed with a cloth, she had had to make her way into the dusty darkness under the stairs—in reality the little Oratory of St. Alexis, but in imagination the cave of some dreadful minotaur—and knock out the black looped webs from the corners. Once a speckled scuttling thing as big as a crab from the beach of Trouville had alighted on her arm, and she had only not screamed because her throat had been paralyzed with terror.

Spiders, and snakes, and other creeping crawling things, the Lord had created them with love, and she must love them too: not, of course, a disproportionate sentimental love, absurdly exalting them, but she must not, even when intimidated, let them disgust her.

The door opens. Sister Aimée springs up, scattering her labels. Doctor La Néele is ushered in by Mother Marie Gonzague and Sister Agnes. His spectacles flash, as does the loop of gold across the tight little drum of his paunch—marriage is evidently suiting him. Cheery bedside greetings. A stethoscope is taken out of a top-hat. It is the new science of auscultation.

He listens gravely to the rattling *râles* in her chest, takes her ivory wand of a wrist in his doctor fingers, narrows his eyes down on to her.

"A slight improvement today, I think."

She gives him a smile as if to say: "That will be nice for those who are anxious about me." But in actuality she says nothing. Her intuition has told her she will die young, but if it is God's will that she should recover, so be it. Those nuns who have always doubted the seriousness of her illness will be able to remark: "There! what did I tell you?" But to herself it is a matter of indifference.

Prior to his coming she had been asked to say a few words of edification to the doctor, but the pretentiousness of the idea embarrassed her. "Ah, my mother," she had protested, "that is not my way at all. Let the doctor think what he will; I love nothing so much as simplicity, and hate the contrary. I assure you to do what you ask would come very badly from me."

Because of her precarious condition it had been expected that Dr. La Néele would recommend Extreme Unction to be given immediately, but Thérèse had put up such a show of vitality and cheerfulness that the subject was not even mentioned. He had occasion to fetch something from his carriage, and whilst he was out of the room Sister Agnes admonished her sister gently: "You do not know how to get what you want." Thérèse laughed. "Why should I?" came the pert reply. "I am not in business!"

When Mother Marie and Doctor La Néele had departed, and Sister Agnes had been given permission to remain behind for a few minutes, Thérèse remarked to her: "In my childhood the great events of my life appeared to be far off, as inaccessible as the mountains. When I saw the young girls make their first Communion I said to myself: 'How shall I make my first Communion?' . . . later on: 'How shall I enter Carmel?' . . . and after: 'How shall I take the habit, when shall I make my profession?' Now I say the same thing about dying. . . . With what peace I let them say I am getting better! Last week, when I was able to stand, they thought I was very ill. This week, when I am so exhausted that I am unable to support myself, behold they think I am saved! But what does it matter what they say? . . . I am like a little child at the railway station who is waiting for his father and mother to put him into the train. Alas, they do not come, and the train departs! But there are others, and I shall not lose them all."

Her remarks during this period, when she was almost always too weak to write anything herself, were taken down verbatim by Sister Agnes, who carried a tablet and pencil in her pocket for this purpose, though Thérèse was very uncertain as to its propriety.

From time to time members of the community would ask the young nun questions, exacting and irritating ones on occasion, according to the memorandum, but, although both Thérèse and ourselves might have been spared the more unnecessary demands, such as: 'Would you like to die tonight?' and 'Shall you mind if your face is contorted after death?' we must acknowledge an immense debt of gratitude to Sister Agnes for recording so accurately the precious last words of a saint.

"Whatever one says to me about my approaching death no longer penetrates. God without doubt does not will that I think in the same way as before my illness. At that time such a thought was very necessary and profitable to me, that I know well. But today it is the contrary; He wills me so to abandon myself as to be altogether like a little child who is not disturbed by whatever is done with him.' She was able to say that now; in spite of her previous timidity, which she maintained had sprung from that extreme uneasiness which she had been used to experience when people concerned themselves about her. And as for a fear of death, she wished to know why it should be assumed she should be preserved from it. "I do not

say, like St. Peter," she commented, "*I will never deny Thee.*"
But she was entirely immune from fear of the hereafter. "Little
children are not damned!" Nervousness was different. She had
always suffered from that.

She was reminded of an occasion when she had gone with
her sister to talk to their relatives in the parlor. She had been
too nervous to speak, and yet almost immediately afterwards
she had brought herself to reprimand a novice with a severity
which surprised no one more than herself.

And she was still able to do so if she deemed it fit, in spite
of her extremity of exhaustion. "Attend well to regularity,"
she lectured a group of novices who had come to look at her
for a few minutes. "After you have been to the parlor, do not
stop to exchange your reflections, because then you would become like a family where one is deprived of nothing."

"How wise you are," said one of the girls, eyeing her with
a dreamy romantic look.

"We must not sit sideways on the chairs," came the seemingly irrelevant comment. "It is marked for us."

The young sentimental nun sat up with confused alacrity!

But the saint was equally exacting with herself. In common
with many, she had a great repugnance to warm milk. One day
when Sister Agnes appeared at her bedside with a beaker of the
accustomed opaque white fluid Thérèse revolted. Her sister
sought for some means of persuading her. "Would you drink
it to save my life?" she asked—surely rather unnecessarily?
"Oh! yes . . ." came the shocked and remorseful reply, "and I
am not willing to drink it for the love of God!" Snatching the
nauseating tumbler, she drained it at a gulp.

And it was the same over the matter of the douche. Despite
her realism, the idea of an enema offended her delicate bour-
geois-trained sense of personal modesty. She would have preferred to suffer the consequences of chronic constipation, in-
tailed by the wasting of her organism and the lack of exercise
attendant on being confined to bed; but as distressing as the

physical intimacy was to her, she asked old Sister Aimée to supply the remedy in clear unaffected tones. Having admitted her disgust, she remarked to Sister Agnes: "I asked for it out of faithfulness."

All this may be regarded as rather absurd; it is mentioned in order to show that she had idiosyncrasies like most people, so that in her case this comparatively simple matter was, in fact, an embarrassing and painful ordeal.

But as far as her soul's tranquillity was concerned, it was no more than anything else. The following statement applied to everything: "My heart is filled with the will of God; when something pours down on it outside, it does not penetrate within, it is a nothing that runs off easily, it is like oil that cannot mix with water. In the depths of my soul I always rest in a profound sleep which nothing can disturb."

2

The slow months wore on. It was summer now. "But," as she remarked patiently, "from moment to moment it is possible to suffer much."

The long days of heat seemed almost static. Lying in bed, as the sun burned through the hours, she was aware of great activity all around her. The noises at this time of year seemed louder. She heard a group of novices crossing the yard below on their way to the fields to toss the hay under the apple trees. They were chattering and laughing like the incessant exuberant morning birds. In the afternoons it was quieter. Mother Aimée dozed over some task, her long nose nodding nearer and nearer to the crumpled linen in her lap. She made a funny zz-ing noise like a bee that had got in and was feebly protesting against the hot window-pane.

The flies were very troublesome. There was a manure heap placed, most inappropriately, near the wall. They came in on waves of pungent smell. Out of a sense of primitive hygiene, and knowing Thérèse's distaste for insects, a swatter had been provided, but she never once raised it. Her love extended now to the lowest form of God's creation. "Leave them in peace," she said to a nun who, seeing how irritating they were, buzzing and hovering, and settling on the saint's mouth and eyelids, clapped her hands about the pillow (this too must have been somewhat disturbing) to shoo them away. "They are my only enemies, and as God has commanded us to forgive our enemies, I am very glad to find an occasion to do so. That is why I always spare them. . . ."

The roses were her greatest consolation. Some think of her as the Rose Queen, she loved them so much. Mother Marie Gonzague, who herself was curiously indifferent to flowers, was thoughtful enough to see that her little daughter was always provided with at least one vase of her adored blooms. She did not have to look to know they were there. The tiniest movement of air brought their presence to her in delicious whiffs of perfume.

Was it a sin of sensuality to take such pleasure in breathing in this exquisiteness? She had had the same qualms about the clear water-fresh scent of the violets in the springtime. She remembered an occasion during the long journey to Rome when a lady had offered her a bottle of eau-de-cologne, and although she had declined had insisted on dashing her brow and temples with the astringent stinging fragrance. It had been heavenly. That, she admitted to Sister Agnes, before making a general confession and recapitulating all the sins of her past life, had certainly been wrong.

On first thoughts one is inclined to pooh-pooh such an idea as a prudish scruple—but what is a sin? She must have known if this apparently slight circumstance, which could have been a source of innocent joy, had really stained her conscience. If it were possible for what looked like murder to be, because of the perpetrators' intention, an act of virtue, then, according to the same broadminded interpretation of human conduct, was it not also possible to damn oneself with a bottle of eau-de-cologne? Possible, but rather unlikely, one surmises.

However, she did not plague herself overmuch with the pleasure of the roses. They were so lovely. She would make the effort of turning her head, which seemed fastened to the pillow by an iron rivet, and look straight into a heart of beauty. She admired the dark red ones particularly: their gradually opening convolutions, velvet-glowing, purple-shaded passages, sometimes decorated with a glistening film of water, nests of warm delicate-textured petals one could have curled up in, carrying the vision round and down to the golden center of fragrance, which was like a home, a crown, and a throne.

The rose did something to symbolize her soul's longing for the Beatific Vision. And it reminded her also of Christ's Passion. Its deep wound was like His riven Heart, the heavy dropping leaves His precious Blood falling. And then sometimes the rose seemed life itself, the whole world singing and moving and refulgent with praises. . . .

Nature had always delighted her, as it had the Mother of Carmel, St. Teresa of Avila. But she knew the sweetness of plants and the grandeur of landscapes, the appealing characteristics of animals (how endearing that childhood knurl-coated lamb had been, and her gift-flecked bantams, and musically-winged doves . . . she remembered her spaniel's soft snuffly kisses . . . this year, on the anniversary of her Profession, a robin had hopped in through the window, alighting for a few seconds on the rail of her bed), they were merely shadows of the joys God has in store for them that love Him.

One day when she was so depressed that she was unable to hide it, and in evident need of some distraction for her grey thoughts, she requested Sister Agnes to read her something out of the life of a saint.

"Would you like the life of St. Francis of Assisi?" she was asked. "That would please you; he speaks of flowers and little birds."

"Oh no," she answered, with that sudden naïve gravity which could fall across her lightness as quickly as a dropped veil, ". . . not for that . . . but to have examples of humility." The preservation of that virtue was all she cared about now.

One warm afternoon her three sisters, sitting beside her bed, had nodded off. When they jerked awake again she raised a humorously admonishing forefinger. "Peter, James, and John!" she said. Her sense of fun was still audacious.

Were her sisters startled on another occasion when she turned to them with a clear frank smile, and said quietly and simply, but with unmistakable conviction: "You know you are nursing a little saint?" She was perhaps the only saint who has had the humility to admit it. That it was humility we may be certain. In any case, was she not right? The reason she was able to make that pronouncement about herself without impairing its truth was because she was dying now, and had spent the whole of her rational life in complete subjection to the Will of God and obedience to her superiors. She had not made herself into a saint. God had done it. Very well, then. So be it. Blessed be His Holy Name!

Many people have mistaken ideas about saints. The essence of sanctity does not lie in heroic virtue, but in that abiding love of God which makes the creature want to obey him. That is why Thérèse prayed incessantly for faithfulness. When someone asked her what dangers of unfaithfulness she might have found herself in, she replied:

". . . A thought of pride voluntarily entertained, as, for example, this: I have acquired such a virtue, and I am certain I have the power to practise it; for then I should be supporting myself on my own strength, and when one does that one risks falling into the abyss. If I were to say: 'My God, I love You so much (and You know it) that I could not listen to one single thought against the Faith,' my temptations would become so violent that I should most certainly go under.

"But if I am humble, I have the right, without offending God, of falling into little follies until the day of my death.

"Look at little children; they never cease from breaking things, tearing their clothes, or falling down, all the while loving their parents very much. Oh, when I fall thus, like a little child, that makes me put my finger on my nothingness, and I say to myself: 'What will happen to me if I try to support myself on my own strength?'

"I can understand very well how St. Peter fell. Poor St. Peter! He trusted in himself instead of trusting in the strength of God. I am sure, if he had humbly said to Jesus, 'I beseech you to give me the courage to follow you unto death,' that courage would have been granted him immediately. I am sure, too, that Our Lord taught no more to His Apostles by His instructions and His visible presence than He teaches to us by the inspiration of His grace. He might well have said to St. Peter: 'Ask of me the strength to accomplish what you would do.' But, no, since He destined Peter to govern the whole Church, in which there are so many sinners, He willed that he should experience in himself what a man is without the grace of God.

"That is why before his fall Jesus said to him, *When thou art converted confirm thy brethren,* that through the recollection of that sin, he might show them by his own experience the feebleness of human strength."

And again, when Sister Agnes said how many struggles she must have been through to attain the degree of perfection in which they saw her, she replied, in an indefinable accent: "Oh, it is not that! Holiness does not consist in this or that practice; it consists in a disposition of the heart, which makes us always humble and little in the hands of God, well aware of our feebleness but confident to audacity in the Father's goodness."

Despite the mysterious powers of rallying which were made manifest in her when it did not seem possible, it was considered prudent to postpone the day of Viaticum and Extreme Unction no longer.

On the morning of the 31st July the convent priest entered the infirmary, which had been scrupulously swept and polished and sweetened with flowers in honor of the Divine Visitor, carrying the pix in his bosom and the vial of Holy Oil.

Her bedside table had now taken on the semblance of an altar. Her few books and necessary articles had been tidied away, and in their place, arranged on a white linen cloth, the appurtenances of the ceremony had been set out. Two holy candles, their flames hardly visible in the brilliant sunshine, stood one either side, with a small raised crucifix in the middle . . . a napkin, a little bowl and ewer with water, some dabs of cotton-wool on a salver for the application of the chrism, and a piece of bread for the priest to wipe his fingers on.

It was a solemn yet smiling occasion. An atmosphere of extraordinary peace seemed to have enveloped the room as in a gold cloud. The devil and his angels were no doubt waiting beyond, but seemed powerless to make felt their grasping presences of evil. It was not until her soul would spring forth naked of the body that they would pounce all together in a united but frustrated effort to carry it off to damnation . . . perhaps they knew it would not be today, and were satisfied to grin and sneer and wait.

The priest splashed their invisibleness with holy water, which must have caused them to writhe as under acid, but to the sick rose it was like soothing dew. Yes, she was more than ever like a white rose this morning, or perhaps her glistening pallor was more like that of a lily?

> *"Thou shalt sprinkle me with hyssop, Lord, and I shall be cleansed;*
> *Thou shalt wash me, and I shall be made whiter than snow."*

At any rate, she appeared to have been visited by that "sudden lightening before death" and seemed as beautiful as she had ever been, though stranger.

She had made her confession previously. There was nothing left to confess now.

The priest held up the silver penny of the Host—the sum of her journey-money.

"Behold the Lamb of God; behold Him who taketh away the sins of the world.
DOMINE NON SUM DIGNUS. . . ."

She was still unworthy, like all of us.

"Receive, sister, the Viaticum of the Body of Our Lord Jesus Christ, that He may protect thee from the malicious foe, and bring thee safe into everlasting life. Amen."

She received. The priest washed his hands and, as is customary, so that no speck of God shall be sullied, she swallowed the ablution also.

The Sacrament of Extreme Unction followed immediately. This could have been the means of restoring her to health, and she was prepared for it, although for the last year her hopes of happiness had been set on heaven. Oil symbolized health, as when it was used by athletes to make their limbs supple and agile, and consecration, as when it was poured on the brows of kings.

"Through this holy anointing and through His most tender mercy may the Lord forgive thee whatsoever thou hast done wrong . . . through . . ." and then followed the touching and blessing of each inlet of the senses through which she might have allowed sin to pass, the eyes, the nostrils, the lips, the hands and the feet.

"Domine Sancte. O holy Lord, Father Almighty, eternal God, who by pouring the blessing of Thy grace into such bodies dost in Thy manifold tenderness preserve the work of Thy hands; in kindness draw Thou near at our calling on Thy name, and free Thy servant from her sickness and give her health, and by Thy right hand uplift her, by Thy strength estab-

*lish her, and by Thy power protect her, and restore her to Thy
Church with all the well-being that she hopes for through
Christ, our Lord. Amen."*

That prayer would be answered in a little while now by
God's not only taking away her disease but the corrupt body
containing it.

Hardly had she time to make her thanksgiving before the
community were bobbing round the door for signs of the
sacrament's effect. It was the sort of interference she was now
resigned to.

After this she could no longer receive Holy Communion
as frequently as she had been wont because of continual bouts
of sickness. He came to her in the Holy Wafer for the last
time on the 19th August, and she made of it an instance of
her curious compulsion to offer her graces for the outcasts of
the world. Despite her cold bearing towards sin itself, she had
a warm and compassionate love of sinners, as must have been
already remarked. It will be remembered that the saint's first
"spiritual child" had been the murderer Pranzini, and how
she had never ceased to have masses said for the repose of the
soul of her "naughty boy." Her last "spiritual child," as far
as her earthly life was concerned, was an outcast not only of
the world but, what was more terrible, of the Church itself.

Père Hyacinthe Loyson was an apostate priest. Thérèse had
prayed for him ever since she had first heard of him in her
nineteenth year. Even then she had been certain that one day
the dreadful interdict of excommunication would be lifted and
the poor tortured soul would be home again with God.

The thought of him began to dominate the prayers of her
last days, and she offered her final Communion for his good.
It was the second half of the clasp binding her necklace of
sinners, a murderer of bodies, and a murderer of his own soul.
We write the last phrase conscious that such may not have

been the case, but that was the pronouncement, even if erroneous, which had been made against him.

God accepted the sacrifice, as he had in the case of Pranzini. On the 9th February, 1912, Hyacinthe Loyson died at the age of eighty-five years, still under major excommunication. As with the first "child" her prayers did not apparently take effect until the last minutes. The old man expired repeating the invocation: "O my sweet Jesus."

The following details were given under all reserves to the Lisieux Carmel.

From the abbey of St. Maurice at Clervaux, the 19th August, 1912: "At the moment of the unhappy man's death, a privileged soul saw him supernaturally enlightened upon the whole extent of the sins of his life. This sight was the occasion of a terrifying temptation to despair over which, happily, he triumphed."

That Père Hyacinthe's soul was safe was also confirmed by Père Flamerion, S.J., grand exorcist of France, the 25th August, 1912.

3

The color of the long days ·began to change. A veil-like distillation hung over the sun, so that his rays, which had been crackling-fierce like a drum, were become quiet and lambent, the slowly swung sticks of a tortoise-shell fan, and the treetops that had glittered as sharp as cut-out metal were softened and blurred with an edge as of lacey gold. The sky was still blue, but with the opacity of an agate.

She stared up and into it so long they thought she enjoyed visions of heaven, but it was the material heaven only she saw, God's heaven was still closed to her as by a barrier of impenetrable iron.

It was the pause of the year, the ripening and crowning, when all seemed held timelessly, and man's mortality, because it seemed nearer, symbolized by the still hidden but no longer so far off winter, gave an added poignancy to the appearances of creatures and things.

She made wreaths for statues of prickly-bearded wheat, and rose-haws, and the first berries. The last flowering of the roses hung out of their bowl with a soft hugeness, pink and golden cloud shapes. The big petals occasionally fell with a faint audible tap, like flakes of nacre.

Sounds and voices echoed, shadows were longer, a kind of invisible harp-string stretched in the air from which the least disturbance, a foot on the gravel below, the turning of the page of a book, the rustling of a habit, shook a vibration as of mysterious music.

There were times when her pain, both physical and mental, was so terrible she felt she might go mad; only last night she had had to beg Our Lady to hold her head for her, the only silent prayer she had been capable of. But now, this afternoon —the weather seemed always afternoon now—she was cast up on one of those rare isles of langor. Sister Agnes glided in thinking she was sleeping. She seemed to be walking on golden water. They sat and talked. It appeared poor Sister Marie of St. Joseph, from whom the news of Thérèse's illness had been, as far as possible, kept hidden, for fear it should have a bad effect on her, had begun to suspect something frightening about the continual absence of her little mentor. She had stuck out her compressed lips, and refused to eat, and when the Prioress herself had come to admonish and reassure her, had tried to hide on one of the shelves of the linen cupboard. Sister Agnes wondered if Thérèse could possibly write the poor soul a little letter . . . ?

Reaching out for her pad and pencil among the small collection of belongings on the bedside table, she disturbed her St. John of the Cross, and a card fell out on her lap. She looked at it, then held it out to Sister Agnes. It was a small picture of Our Lady of Victories, to whom the successful novena had been made when she was so ill as a child. On the back of it she had fastened the tiny white flower her father had gathered from the garden-wall on the day she had told him of her vocation, ten years ago. It was thin and withered now, the petals quite transparent. Sister Agnes took it and gazed at it, reminiscently.

She noticed the stem near the root had snapped.

CHAPTER FIVE

The Beginning

I

SEPTEMBER 30TH, 1897. A more important date than that recording a monarch or a victory, the date of the death of a saint.

Sister Agnes, who has been watching all night, draws back the curtain to peer out at a gashed and weeping dawn. The wound in the sky is livid as if drained of blood. Against it the tops of the thinning chestnuts and the sharp spear-headed gable of one of the yard-buildings stand out greyly in outline.

The water-drops fly in, momentarily refreshing her taut sleepless face. There is a gurgling in the gutters, drowning the intermittent twittering of the waking birds who seem reluctant to sing. Most of them have flown away to sunnier lands. Another bird will be migrating soon. . . .

Had she but an inkling of the golden future, the earthly future of titles and honors, awaiting her little sister, Sister Agnes would be perhaps less aware of the dreariness of the rain-etched view. It would be as nothing perhaps. But she would still be sad. Perhaps it was a sin to mourn a soul so clearly destined for heaven? So be it. . . . Sister Agnes' heart was stooping with sorrow.

Well, at least her sister shall not die today. She has prophesized fine weather for her departure, and by the look of the somber piled clouds the rain will continue until it is dark again. But Sister Agnes should know that the weather and the vagaries of the good God are unpredictable. Thérèse, not yet twenty-five, will die today, and it will have stopped raining. Tonight the stars will shine in a clear washed sky.

But there will be a little eternity to traverse before that

moment. We use the word little to effect some kind of comparison, but actually the pain and agony of these last hours will be such as to lift them out of time entirely.

It is humid, typical autumn Normandy weather. The little nun lies with her eyes closed, but she is enjoying no respite from consciousness. Her breath issues in a slow whistle, like a distant siren. It is at the same time ludicrous, terrifying, and depressing, the slow-drawn wobbly note so impersonal and mechanical as to suggest a curious machine concealed in her throat for recording the gradually fading percussion of life.

Sister Agnes, during the long watches, must have felt an almost maternal agony, as she sat hour after hour by the side of Thérèse, unable to do very much to relieve her physical suffering, and nothing as regards the incomprehensible torments of her martyred soul. The responsibility of motherhood had been placed on her by Thérèse herself twenty years ago, and she had not faltered in her duties for an instant. She it was who had prepared her for her first Communion, and attended to all her childhood wants, until the call from Carmel had become too insistent to disregard any longer, and until Thérèse joined her there, had had to retire behind the grille and direct her child-sister by proxy. Once Thérèse became a postulant, although it had been necessary for Pauline to keep an uncreaturely distance, she had found plenty of means to indicate the way for her "daughter," and then when she was elected Prioress, and Thérèse's spiritual mother indeed, it had been much easier.

She came back to the foot of the bed, and looked so deeply into the ravaged face on the pillow before her, with such a magnitude of compassion that, as it would have been with Thérèse's real mother had she been alive and able to be there, it was as if she were searching to draw the throbbing core of suffering out of the young girl and into her own being.

Gradually the dim dawn light brightened, though it still continued to pour with rain. Thérèse opened her eyes, and by a prodigious effort turned up the corners of her bitten mouth into a semblance of the famous smile. The murmur of the Mass from the chapel below floated up through the bare floor boards, and Sister Agnes remained, making the responses mentally, as she resumed her position on the stiff upright chair. As a sacrifice on behalf of her darling she had declined Mother Marie Gonzague's offer of a more comfortable one.

Today was not the day of the doctor's visit. After Mass the Prioress would come, and in their turn Sister Marie and Sister Geneviève, Thérèse's young cousin, Sister Marie of the Eucharist, whose youth and airy ways, coupled with a voice like a blackbird's, were already beginning to endear her to the community; they, and other nuns not bound by the ties of blood, some drawn more out of curiosity than affection, would all come and lean over her and smile at her, and ask her how she was, in most cases begging words of comfort rather than being able to give any.

Although she seemed too weak to do anything but remain prostrate, she forced herself to sit up, a stool pushed behind her pillows, and even to talk to them occasionally in a voice no longer clear and pure as a clarinet, but reduced to an almost inaudible hoarse whisper, so that to her last words was added a queer dramatic quality, as if she were imparting secrets.

It was very close. She was in such a ferment all the time that the mattress was saturated with perspiration. The struggle to breathe was causing her acute distress, so that she constantly moaned and wrung her hands, but lights of cheerfulness continued to break and pass across her troubled face like beams through fast-travelling clouds. She was being carried along quickly, but the journey seemed static, as if the vehicle were motionless, the landscape unwinding and repeating itself as in a monotonous panorama.

She could not believe she was really going to die, not yet. When she was alone with Sister Agnes she let fall broken statements, which her sense of scandal had made her refrain from uttering in the presence of the less intelligent members of the community.

"See, what strength I have today! . . . No, I am not going to die yet. Perhaps months await me. I do not believe it is death, but more suffering for me. And tomorrow it will be worse. Ah, so much the better."

At intervals she would stare at the statue of Our Lady which had been placed on a bracket over her bed, her eyes so dilated with yearning that her sister could hardly bear to look at her. "O, my good Holy Virgin, come to my aid. . . . Oh, my God!" Here she would almost shriek, as if she were being gnawed by wild beasts; then, more quietly, in utter exhaustion and abandonment: "I love Him, the good God. . . ." Then the scorching tide of pain would rise again, and she would writhe so much she would knock the stool on to the floor. "If this is the agony, what then will death be like?" She was obviously terrified. All consolation had been taken away from her. She felt completely alone, left to the mercilessness of these trampling fiends, who were bent on dragging her down, down into bottomless oblivion. And yet she could call out as the martyr's wheel smashed and resmashed her: "My God, do all your will! . . . My God, my God, you are so good! Oh yes, you are so good! I know it!"

They are almost beyond human comprehension, these cries of love in circumstances where it would seem love itself must lie battered and broken—dead; but such is the mysterious paradox of true spirituality that it can honestly be said a saint is happy in such suffering, finds her happiness there, because the suffering is borne for love. However it may seem to the unenlightened, there is no morbidity, no perverted sensationalism, only intensest joy, the outcome of sacrifice which is as far as love can go before entering into that state of eternal ecstasy, the beating Heart of Love itself, the contemplation of the Beatific Vision of God.

If, ultimately, it were not a gift, it might be said that little

Thérèse was intent on buying mankind's happiness, ransoming it from hell with the substance of her very soul.

We need not be horrified. It was her own choice. Maybe no more is asked from us than to look on . . . but let us turn away for a moment and regard the ruined Eden these pangs are repairing, making up, if it were possible, what might have been missing from the Passion of Christ.

How tragic, how pathetic is the world, and how pathetic man's efforts to keep pace with the continual decaying, the continual wasting away. That Old Bawd, our Mother Eve, raddled and patched out of all recognition, screams and laughs her admonition and encouragement to us, so that deceived by hedonism and progress, but still slaves to her material and illusory desires, we invent new cures for our diseases, and build rockets to the moon, but all to no purpose—we shall never, of ourselves, escape the consequences of the fall.

Look at the ever-rising tide of dust, it creeps in everywhere. . . . And the Queens of Glamor or Respectability must eat and excrete with the worst of us, and in the end She who rules armies and kingdoms will be no more than her victim, the tattered scorched woman rummaging her wooden spoon in the garbage-bins. . . . The tide of obliterating dust will have become one with, will have covered us all.

And yet we live as heedlessly as if we were never to die. Ah, but we are only too aware of it. Hence the clamor and the clangor as we try to build up ramparts of power and vanity to ward off My Lord Nothing, who will demolish us, when it is his whim, as with "a little pin."

It is the saints who hold the secret of the only remedy. Let us have recourse to them, and we will be happy, as Thérèse is, even in our error and dying, because we will know something of what our disappointment means, and the joy of the fulfilled promises of Christ.

At three o'clock in the afternoon Mother Marie Gonzague came and placed a picture of Our Lady of Mount Carmel on her daughter's knees. Thérèse crossed her hands over her breast, as if she would save old Sister Aimée that trouble when the time came to prepare her corpse. She had already glimpsed her palliasse outside in the anteroom, and had smiled at the thought of what it had been brought down for. Her eyes, enormous as great wells of infinite depth, turned as simply as a child's to the watching Prioress.

It was her wish that she should expire in the arms of Mother Marie Gonzague, thus avoiding the temptation of succumbing to a too human comfort at the last, such as she would have certainly felt in the embrace of her own sister. But she was to die in the invisible arms of God. Sister Geneviève had rhapsodized on the theme of angels descending and bearing her away on their wings. "You will not see them," had been Thérèse's dry comment. But there was no room for acerbity in her speech at this moment.

"Oh, my mother, present me very soon to the Blessed Virgin. Prepare me to die well."

Mother Marie Gonzague replied that she had always understood and practised humility and therefore her preparation had been made already.

Thérèse appeared to be considering. Eventually she remarked quite lightly, as if it had all been settled in any case: "Yes, quite so, I have never sought anything but the truth. . . . Yes, I have understood humility of heart."

Later, she turned to Sister Agnes, who, as soon as the dying nun opened her mouth to speak, brought out her pencil and note-book with the alacrity of a reporter. A reporter might have given much to be there had all the facts been known. Yet how often do we hear of sanctity making headlines?

The elder nun's detachment must have been heroic.

"All that I have written about my desire for suffering— have you got that?"

". . . desire for suffering . . . yes?"

"It is quite true. I shall never repent of having delivered myself up to Love."

From that moment it seemed to Sister Agnes that the frail figure on the bed, lapped about by the weird storm-light falling in dramatically through the window, so that the scene had taken on the exaltation of a holy picture, was no longer suffering herself, but like the martyrs of old, luminous and ecstatic under the hands of their executioners, was imbued with a divine power sustaining, or anesthetizing her through her exorbitant torments.

She spoke again, as out of an incandescent cloud:

"I would not have believed it possible to suffer so much! Never! Never! I can only explain it by the ardent desires I have had to save souls. . . ."

There was a terrible struggling pause.

"I cannot breathe, I cannot die. . . ."

Then, with perfect resignation:

"I am willing to suffer more."

Another hour passed. The rain beat on the glass like the devil's drum summoning all the fiends from hell to make a last onslaught on her departing soul.

She groaned, then spoke again with the most extraordinary clarity:

"All my smallest desires have been realized. . . . Then the greatest of all must be realized—to die of love. . . ."

At five o'clock Sister Agnes had been left to watch with her alone. Suddenly the face on the pillow changed with an unmistakable sinking. The light was fading out of it. It was the agony. There was no time to be lost. Sister Agnes has recorded it thus:

"I summoned the Community to come in haste to the infirmary. . . .

"She greeted all the sisters with a sweet smile. She held her crucifix firmly in her hands, and kept her eyes fixed upon it. For more than two hours the terrible death rattle tore her chest. Her features were congested, her hands purple, her feet were icy cold, and she trembled in every limb. The death sweat stood out in great drops on her forehead and coursed down her face. The ever-increasing oppression made her utter feeble involuntary cries in her efforts to breathe. Thinking to moisten her parched lips, Sister Geneviève of the Holy Face placed a small particle of ice upon them. No one could ever forget the look of heavenly sweetness with which our little saint regarded 'Céline' at that moment. It was like a sublime encouragement, a supreme adieu.

"At six o'clock the Angelus sounded, and she raised her eyes pleadingly towards the statue of the Blessed Virgin.

"At a few minutes after seven o'clock, thinking that the end was yet some way off, Mother Prioress dismissed the assembled Community.

"She sighed and said:

" 'My mother, is it not yet the agony? Am I not yet going to die?'

" 'Yes, my child, it is the agony; but perhaps the good God wills to prolong it for some hours."

"She answered courageously:

" 'Ah, well! . . . so be it; so be it! . . . Oh! I do not wish to suffer less.'

"Then, looking at her crucifix:

" 'Oh! . . . I love Him! My God! . . . I . . . love . . . Thee!'

"Scarcely had she uttered these words when she fell gently back, her head inclined a little to the right. We thought that all was over, and our mother had the infirmary bell sounded in haste to call the Community back. 'Open all the doors,' she exclaimed. These words seemed to have a singularly solemn significance at such a moment, and I thought that in heaven Our Lord was repeating the same words to His angels.

"The sisters came and knelt round the bed. . . .

"The face of our saint assumed again the lily-like tint which it had possessed when she was in full health; her eyes remained fixed on high, irradiated and expressing such happiness as surpassed all her desires. She made certain movements with her head, as if at intervals she was divinely wounded by the shafts of love.

"After that ecstasy, which lasted for the space of a *Credo*, she closed her eyes. . . ."

Suddenly the rain ceased, and the last sun flooded the room with a golden glow. Myriads of birds began singing.

2

It is her feast again.

The flickering, stumbling procession winds on through the narrow broken ways. The sceptical, or weary, gaze down in muted curiosity.

We pass gaps, heaps of shards, new scaffolding.

Sordidness, depression, hope, faint and stooping, like the candles. Some have gone out.

Ahead, the gold casket seems tossed on crying human waves.

"*Sainte Thérèse, hâtez-vous de nous exaucer!*
Sainte Thérèse, revenez dans ce monde qui se meurt. . . ."

Thus may mankind continue to implore her aid and protection until the end of time.

What more remains?

We lay down our pen with a sense of inadequacy. It is not by writing books that the life of a saint is revealed. There is only one way to know St. Thérèse, the only way really to know anyone. It was the way which gave her her own remarkable insight into the souls she met.

It is the Way of Love.